THE AUDUBON
NATURE
ENCYCLOPEDIA

THE AUDUBON NATURE ENCYCLOPEDIA

SPONSORED BY THE NATIONAL AUDUBON SOCIETY

VOLUME 5

GR-IN

CURTIS BOOKS
A division of
The Curtis Publishing Company
Philadelphia — New York

CREATED AND PRODUCED BY
COPYLAB PUBLISHING COUNSEL, INC., NEW YORK

Copyright © 1965
by
National Audubon Society, Inc.

PICTORIAL ACKNOWLEDGEMENTS, Volume 5

Edmund J. Sawyer, 793 —Robert Jackowitz, 796 —M. Woodbridge Williams, 795 (courtesy of National Park Service) —George Porter*, 804, 923, 927, 991 —Allan D. Cruickshank*, 803, 808, 813, 890, 899, 917 —Jack E. Boucher, 807 (courtesy of National Park Service) —Elsa and Henry Potter, 824 top left —Karl Maslowski*, 872, 970 top right —Roland C. Clement, 834 —J. M. Johnson*, 819 —United States Department of Agriculture, 887 right, 798, 799, 839, 921, 926, 936, 937, 941 top, 945 bottom, 947, 949, 951, 924, 966, 967, 968, 969, 982, 984, 985, 986 —Bruce Horsfall, 822, 826 —F. L. Jaques, 831 —Allan Brooks, 811, 814, 815, 816, 845, 864, 865, 868 —W. D. Berry, 818, 841 —Lee Adams, 817, 849, 855, 860 —Joe Van Wormer*, 827, 873, 874 top —Hugh M. Halliday, 874 mid left —Don S. Heintzelman, 874 bottom —R. T. Peterson*, 824 bottom, 829, 862, 867, 868, 897, 904, 907, 912, 915 —John K. Terres, 852, 853 bottom, 878, 945 top —Michael H. Bevans, 835, 857, 858, 877 —United States Department of Agriculture (courtesy of Soil Conservation Service), 853 top —Kenneth Middleham, 876 —J. A. Starkey, 887 left —L. M. Chace*, 889 —Lena H. Scott, 850, 891 —National Park Service, 880 —Louis Agassiz Fuertes, 893 —Ernest J. Borgman, 903 top (courtesy of National Park Service) —Hugh Dell Muller, 910 bottom (courtesy of National Park Service) —G. Ronald Austing*, 901 —Grace A. Thompson*, 918 —Bernard L. Gluck*, 929 —M. Vinciquerra*, 932 —W. J. Jahoda*, 941 bottom —Ray Glover*, 942, 950 —B. W. McFarland, 958 —Karl Maslowski and Woodrow Goodpaster*, 962 bottom —W. J. Breckenridge*, 963 —Enid Furlonger, 968-969 —Lee Jenkins*, 971 —Suzan N. Swain, 974, 975, 976, 977 (courtesy of Smithsonian Institute), 972, 973 —Leonard Lee Rue, III*, 990 —Betty Barford*, 992 top right —Robert Hermes*, 992 left top and bottom —Olin S. Pettingill, Jr., 900

*Photographs from Photo-Film Department of National Audubon Society

The common grackle invades urban areas to feed on lawns

Common grackles have long, wedge-shaped tails creased down the middle

GRACKLE
Common Grackle
Other Common Names—Blackbird, crow blackbird, keel-tailed grackle
Scientific Name—*Quiscalus quiscula*
Family—Icteridae (meadowlarks, black-birds, and orioles)
Order—Passeriformes
Size—Length, 11 to 13 inches
Range—Breeds east of the Rockies from Great Slave Lake, northern Manitoba, and Newfoundland south to the Gulf

Coast and Florida. Winters from northern United States (casually) south to southern Texas, Mississippi, Alabama, southern Georgia, and Florida Keys

The "mud season" of early spring is also blackbird season. The dark feathered tribes push northward from the southern states close on the heels of retreating winter. They journey a few miles each day over the open countryside, following up the melting snows, only tarrying when late storms block their progress. By the first of March, they reach the northern borders of the United States. Most of the later spring migrants, such as the warblers and the orioles, move north during the nights as if by schedule; those birds that migrate in the very early spring, such as the robins and the blackbirds, travel by day. Their date of arrival will vary by as much as two or three weeks, depending on whether spring is early or late.

The northward-moving flocks soon scatter over the countryside. Pairs of common grackles can be seen walking about sedately on lawns in a pigeon-toed manner, with their tails held high. The grackle is one of the two or three most common native lawn birds in some sections, particularly in the Midwest. They are everywhere—along shady city streets in the towns, about farm buildings, and along the fences that border the fields.

The grackles are the largest of the blackbirds. They have long, wedge-shaped tails that are creased down the middle, suggesting the keel of a boat. The common grackle is not much of a songster but, besides the *chuck* or *chack* notes that are common to all the blackbirds, it makes another call that can hardly be interpreted as anything else but a song. It is heard at no other time of the year but spring and only for a short time after its arrival. With great effort the glossy black male utters his most accomplished vocal effort, a harsh, squeaky note that sounds like the creaking of a hanging sign or a rusty pulley.

For all the common grackles that seem to be around, very few nests are seen. This is because they like to gather in little colonies, often in a dense, ornamental grove of evergreens. The grove might be on the edge of a farm, on an estate, or in a city park. Where there are no dense evergreens to build in, they will nest in densely-leaved broad-leaved trees, in bushes and even in hollow trees.

The nest is bulky, larger and deeper than a robin's nest, from which it can easily be distinguished by its lack of mud. Twigs and weeds make up the walls: grasses the lining. The 4 to 6 eggs are about 1¼ inches long, pale green or pale red-brown and sparingly daubed with dark spots and scrawls, which look as if they had been applied with a scratchy pen. The female, duller and less glossy than her mate, broods the eggs for 14 or 15 days.

Like the young of all songbirds, newly born grackles are blind and helpless, without a single feather to cover their nakedness. Their necks are long and wobbly, their mouths enormous, but after only a few days they feather out and look more attractive. The bobtailed youngsters have none of the sleek glossiness of their parents. They are very plain, sooty-brown in color.

Nesting over, the grackle families band together, spreading in black battalions over the fields. Although they do eat grain, they also eat many crop-destroying insects. Many weeks before the fall migration gets under way, grackles gather in great roosts with other blackbirds. They congregate nightly, flock after flock pouring in from all points of the compass, 20 or 30 miles around. Some roosts number millions of birds. Very few common grackles stay through the winter in colder parts of United States. A.B.,Jr

A view of Grand Canyon National Park from the north rim

GRAND CANYON NATIONAL PARK

Location—Northwestern Arizona

Size—1,009 square miles

Mammals—Mountain lions, mule deer, pronghorns, bobcats, coyotes, ringtails, rabbits, foxes, badgers, Kaibab and Abert's squirrels

Bird life—Bald eagles, golden eagles, roadrunners, quails, hummingbirds, jays, orioles, many others

Plants—Cacti, mesquites, sages, willows, pinyon and ponderosa pines

The Colorado River, perhaps seven million years ago, was a slow moving stream flowing through a relatively flat plain. The landmass in the entire region rose, and the river cut through the rock at a faster rate. Landslides and the forces of erosion began to cut the side valleys and canyons, adding more rock to the grinding effect of the water.

The highest point on the rim is 9,100 feet above sea level, the lowest 1,850 feet. The canyon is 217 miles long; about 105 miles of it is within the park, and the average depth is a mile. The width varies from 4 to 18 miles.

Accommodations—Hotel, lodge, cabins, and public campgrounds within park; horses and mules, and guides, available

Headquarters—On the south rim, at Grand Canyon, Arizona

Ragged peaks rise above Jenny Lake at Grand Teton National Park in Wyoming

GRAND TETON NATIONAL PARK

Location—Northwestern Wyoming
Size—484 square miles
Mammals—Moose, elks, bighorn sheep, bison, grizzly bears, black bears, mule deer, badgers, martens, beavers, pikas, marmots, coyotes, otters, rabbits
Birdlife—Trumpeter swans, bald eagles, Canada geese, great blue herons, western tanagers, water ouzels, ducks, horned owls, lazuli buntings, black rosy finches,
Plants—Alpine firs, Douglas-firs, spruces, pines, quaking aspens, cotton-woods, Indian paintbrushes, balsam

The Teton Mountain Range, carved by glaciers and erosion, looms above Lake Moran, Jenny Lake, the Snake River, and the rich wildlife area of Jackson Hole. Once a contested hunting ground of various Indian tribes, the region was trapped by the mountain men, grazed by the stockmen, and, in parts, farmed; some of Jackson Hole is still in private hands.

The park has foot trails, horseback trails, and boat trips; mountain climbing is regulated.

Accommodations—Dude ranches and motels are available
Headquarters—Within the park

GRASS

Introduction to Grasses

The grass family includes some of the most economically important plants in the world: the cereals, sugarcane, bamboo, and the forage and ornamental grasses. The cereals are the edible seeds of grasses that have been cultivated for centuries. Of these, wheat, corn, rye, barley, oats, and rice provide most of the breadstuffs of the world.

Most of the valuable pasture plants that provide fodder for flocks and herds are also members of the grass family. Grasses spread themselves over and through the ground by means of horizontal underground stems called rhizomes, a way of growth that is very effective in binding the soil together and preventing erosion.

Grasses grow all over the world, from the equator to the arctic and antarctic regions, and from sea level to the tops of high mountains. They are among the simplest of the flowering plants. The flowers lack sepals and petals and have only stamens and a pistil that is almost hidden under dry, overlapping scales. The stems of grasses are jointed and usually round and hollow. These slender stems can stand up against strong winds and support heavy heads of grain. The stem is reinforced by the sheathing base of the leaf. This important plant family is often ignored by the average student of nature, perhaps because grasses are so common. The seeds and vegetative parts of grasses are highly important as food for many kinds of wildlife. At least 94 kinds of birds and mammals eat the seeds or green parts of wheat alone, one of the cultivated grasses. Brief descriptions of a few species are given here as an introduction to the grasses.

Common Grasses of Pastures

June or Kentucky bluegrass, *Poa pratensis*. This is one of the best pasture grasses and the principal lawn grass of the United States. It is a perennial and produces numerous creeping rhizomes. Growing from one to three feet high, it reaches its most luxuriant growth in the limestone regions of Kentucky.

Timothy, *Phleum pratense*. Timothy is the most important meadow grass grown in North America and is the usual cultivated hay, although it also grows wild. It is an erect, rather stiff grass and the stems bear cylindrical flower spikes, or heads, resembling small green cattails and containing several hundred flowers.

Orchard grass, *Dactylis glomerata*. This coarse, erect, perennial bunch grass attains a height of three feet. It ranks high as a farm grass because it affords good spring pasturage and has a long growing season. The flowers appear in June, the stem growing out of a tuft of leaves.

Redtop, *Agrostis alba*. Redtop is cultivated in the northern United States as pasture grass, especially in soils lacking lime. It is a slender, graceful biennial, growing from two to three feet tall. The panicle has delicate, reddish branches and fields of redtop have a soft purplish or reddish color.

Sweet vernal grass, *Anthoxanthum odoratum*. The fragrance of new-mown hay is due largely to this sweet-scented grass. It has no forage value but is included in forage plantings for the sake of its fragrance. Common in fields, meadows, and along roadsides, this slender, erect perennial has spikelike, brownish-green flower clusters.

Grasses that are Weeds

Some grasses grow where they are undesirable and hence are called weeds.

Foxtail grass, *Setaria* spp. Several species of foxtails are weeds along roadsides and in cultivated ground, but the yellow foxtail is probably the most common. The terminal, cylindric, hairy

Kentucky bluegrass

spikes are characteristic, suggesting hairy caterpillars.

Crabgrass or finger grass, *Digitaria sanguinalis.* Crabgrass is a common weed in lawns, gardens, and cultivated fields. It is an annual, many-branched, straggling species, usually purplish, and bears from 4 to 10 slender spikes, spread out like fingers.

Quack grass or couch grass, *Agropyron repens.* This troublesome weed of fields and meadows is a perennial that spreads rapidly by means of its creeping, yellowish, jointed rhizomes, each joint of which may develop a new plant. Quack grass is green in color and usually grows from 1½ to 3 feet tall, with terminal spikes from 2 to 6 inches in length. This grass is known also as quick grass, quitch grass, scutch grass, twitch grass, and witchgrass.

Timothy

Orchard grass

Foxtail millet

Barnyard grass or cockspur grass, *Echinochloa crusgalli*. Common throughout the country, except at higher altitudes, barnyard grass looks weedy and is a weed. In wet soil it is usually a stout, erect plant, but in dry waste places it is more spreading and sparse-looking. The large terminal flower cluster is commonly purplish-brown.

Recommended Reading

Grass and People—Charles M. Wilson. University of Florida Press, Gainesville, Florida.

Grasses—Alma Moore. Macmillan Company, New York.

Grasses and Grassland Farming—H. W. Staten. Devin-Adair Company, New York.

Grasses of the Southwestern United States—Frank W. Gould. University of Arizona Press, Tucson, Arizona.

GRASSLANDS
Seas of Grass

What was America like 500 years ago— When the early explorers reached the New World they found a continent that had remained virtually unchanged for centuries. At first, to all appearances, it seemed that the whole continent must be forested, but later adventurers discovered that far inland were vast seas of grass. The waving grass stretched from horizon to horizon, domed over by 180 degrees of blue sky. It seemed as if all the flocks and herds in the world could be comfortably pastured on the endless plains and prairies.

In those days America was about half forest land. Most of the other half was grassland; tall grasses in the humid midwestern prairies, shorter grasses in the dry western plains. In some places, especially in the South, grass and trees grew together.

To the millions of people in America, the plains and prairies are as important as the forests, for it is there that most of the wheat, corn, and other cereal crops are raised. These plants are grasses, too. In the drier sections of the country, where these crops would not do so well, cattle and sheep are raised by the millions. This huge inland part of the continent, known as the *range,* is the backbone of the American cattle and sheep industry.

Grass is also a soil builder. A healthy sod has new roots every year. The old decaying roots build up the organic content of the earth much more rapidly than trees do. The vigorous turf holds the deep soil in place and thus keeps it from deteriorating into a desert.

Wildlife and the Range

The environment of a region has a direct bearing on the kind of wildlife living there, and wildlife in return has a beneficial effect on the environment.

When the American explorers, Lewis and Clark, pushed westward, there were herds of bison, or buffalo, as far as the eye could see. Later most people saw these imagnificent beasts only on nickels, although a few bands are still allowed to roam the range (*See under Bison and under Extinct and Threatened Animals of North America*). Cattle have taken the place of the large herds of bison. In many parts of the West, pronghorn antelopes were abundant, also deer and elk. These large grazing animals were just part of the wildlife of the grasslands.

In the main, the mammals and birds all contributed to a healthy balance of the grassland community. The burrowing animals—gophers and prairie dogs for example—increased the porousness of the soil, making it easier for the rain to sink in rather than run off. They were like earthworms in this respect, mixing, loosening, draining, and fertilizing the soil. They did not become too numerous for the good of the grass because coyotes and hawks ate some of them (*See Balance of Nature*). In like manner, grassland birds helped to keep insects within reasonable bounds. (It has been estimated that birds within the range area have a value of more than $200,000,000 in protecting crops.) In many mountain sections, beavers working on the little headwater streams regulated the stream flow to the good advantage of the grass below.

Exploitation of the Range

When one cannot see the limits of a thing it is often thought it has none. Men thought the grasslands were limitless because they seemed to stretch out endlessly beyond all horizons. In time, the range was settled by cattlemen, and the Plains Indians and buffalo gave way to cowboys and cattle. Millions of head of cattle grazed on the nourishing grasses. Big fortunes were made, and in a very short time, by 1885, the range was full. In fact, some places were already overstocked. They were carrying three or four times as many cattle as they could support comfortably.

Then came the sheep. The sheep even

invaded the summer ranges high up in the mountains and ate the tender grasses at the edge of the snow. The cattlemen, hating the competition, had some very serious fights with the sheepmen.

At this point, when the livestock industry had become so dangerously overexpanded, the homesteaders, or farmers, came in. Much of the open range was broken up by them for farms, and the virgin prairie sod was broken by their plows. The development of farm machinery eventually made it possible to plow ground twenty times as quickly as it could be done with a team of horses.

So the Sod Went Out

The range, 40 percent of the United States, has been more than half depleted. Within this vast area of about 728,000,000 acres, it is said that only about one-eighth of it is in satisfactory condition, or not overgrazed. The chief cause of this depletion is too many cattle and sheep.

Agriculture and animal husbandry are necessary to human existence. The nation was growing rapidly at the time that the plains were opened, and more food resources were needed. However, exploitation of the virgin plains and prairies that occurred was much greater than necessary. It became harder and harder to eke a living from the land the more exhausted its fertility became.

Too many cattle check the growth of grass; their paths to water are the beginnings of eroded gullies and arroyos which rapidly carry precious water away from the thirsty sod. Sheep are even more destructive than cattle because their cloven lips enable them to eat right down to the living nub of the grass. They not only check the growth of grass but kill it. In some parts of the West these wooly creatures have been called "hoofed locusts." Meadows on high mountain slopes, destroyed by too many sheep, often turn into dusty crum-

bling bluffs that are an eyesore and unfit for any further use.

Much of the homestead farming was on land that would not be plowed during dry seasons. The soil crumbled away or whirled off into the air; the crops withered and died. The unfortunate people who tilled this soil frequently lost everything they had, could not get enough to eat, and often reached the lowest depths of human misery and degradation. It would have been much better had this land been left to the cattle, but not too many cattle, just enough to increase their weight without destroying the protecting sod. Range management, or control of the numbers of livestock grazing the land, would have perpetuated the grassland and would have protected the soil.

The effect of this exploitation on the abused plains and prairies could be seen on every hand. Many of the native grasses almost disappeared. Willows along the streams were eaten back to the stumps by hungry cattle. Sagebrush began to grow on the exposed soil where it did not grow before. In some parts of the country, weeds that were poisonous to livestock became established. In other sections, thorns and spiny plants had less competition than formerly and were on the increase.

Clouds of Dust

The dust bowl was a large area in the vicinity of Kansas and Oklahoma, where dust storms were especially frequent. Terrible droughts had made the soil powder fine. In many sections there was no sod to hold the soil in place. High dry winds whipped it into the air, the sun was hidden and visibility was less than in a dense fog. From a distance the approaching storm looked like a great billowy black curtain a mile high, a curtain made of the topsoil of thousands of farms. As the dust rolled on, a dense brown pall settled over everything; people became lost and many others contracted lung diseases from breathing particles of dust.

These storms carry off the soil from one state and deposit it in another. More than once the dust from western prairies dimmed the sun over New York City and even in New England. The fine light soil particles, rich in organic matter, are carried the farthest. Instead of enriching the farmlands where they fall, they act as a film which makes rain run off the surface of the soil instead of being absorbed. The heavier inorganic material is left behind, near the origin of the storm. It drifts into sandy dunes which have a tendency to travel and spread.

Wildlife in the Balance

When the range was destroyed, the large mammals were the first to go—for example, the buffalo, pronghorn antelope, and elk. They could not compete with cattle, nor would the cattlemen let them. They wanted every blade of grass for their livestock. For centuries the wild creatures had lived on the plains without irreparably injuring the turf. Now there was no place for them.

As the range became overgrazed, grasshopper plagues became worse. These long-legged insects seem to thrive best when the turf is thin and weedy. Most parasites and predators are seldom out of balance under normal conditions. In similar manner, mice, gophers, and other rodents thrive best when the grassland has been more heavily grazed than it should be. If the range were not grazed beyond its ability to supply enough new growth, the rodents would stay in balance.

Rather than get at the root of the matter, ranchmen went in heavily for poisoning campaigns. By this method they have sought to control the rodent population, but poison is nonselective and kills other creatures as well. To make things worse, coyotes, which eat untold numbers of grasshoppers, mice, and gophers, were shot as well as poisoned. Hawks, like the Swainson's,

rough-legged, and red-tailed—all rodent eaters—were shot wherever they were seen perching along highways on fence posts or utility wires.

At least one species of bird, the masked bobwhite, completely disappeared from its limited range in the United States because overgrazing destroyed the grass country in southern Arizona where it formerly lived.

Many clear streams that formerly abounded in trout became so silted with mud carried from eroded grasslands, and by the loss of vegetation along their banks, that fishes in the streams could no longer survive.

In many mountainous sections beavers were trapped out (*See under Beaver*). Considering their value as conservers of soil and water, this was a mistake. Six hundred beavers, for example, were removed by trappers some years ago from one of the national forests. Very soon after their disappearance, the pasture grass, which was worth $3 to $5 a ton when forested, was reduced from 15,000 tons to a few hundred. Good fishing streams disappeared, and the general water supply lessened. Farms that were dependent on irrigation could no longer get enough water. Although the trappers made $4,000 to $5,000 in one year, the stockmen lost $50,000 each year. By their own figuring they have estimated that whereas a dead beaver was worth $10 or $15, a living one was worth at least $300 for its value in stream control and the building of rich meadowlands in river valleys.

Restoration of the Range

A sharp lesson is often necessary before conditions are corrected. The dust storms of the 1930's, with all the misery they caused to men and animals, were such a lesson. Steps were taken to restore the range. The moving dunes, the bald spots and eroded places were anchored down by the planting of tough grasses that could withstand the climate and bind the soil together. Later, the

Bison once grazed in great numbers in western grasslands

more edible grasses were planted. The reforestation of the upper slopes of mountain streams did much to help, but the most important step of all was to reduce the number of cattle or sheep on the range to within the carrying capacity of the grasslands to support them. This varied a great deal in different parts of the country and on different soils. Cattlemen found that it was better in the long run to have a few less cattle on a piece of land than to have too many—and then through overgrazing to have none at all.

It is said that Americans have not taken as much interest in grasses as the farmers of England. On the other hand, Americans have taken considerable interest in their forests. Trees are dramatic, grass is humble.   —R.T.P.

Recommended Reading

Deserts on the March—Paul B. Sears. University of Oklahoma Press, Norman, Oklahoma.
Our Plundered Planet—Fairfield Osborn (paperback). Little, Brown Company, Boston.
Rich Land, Poor Land—Stuart Chase. McGraw-Hill Book Company, Inc., New York.

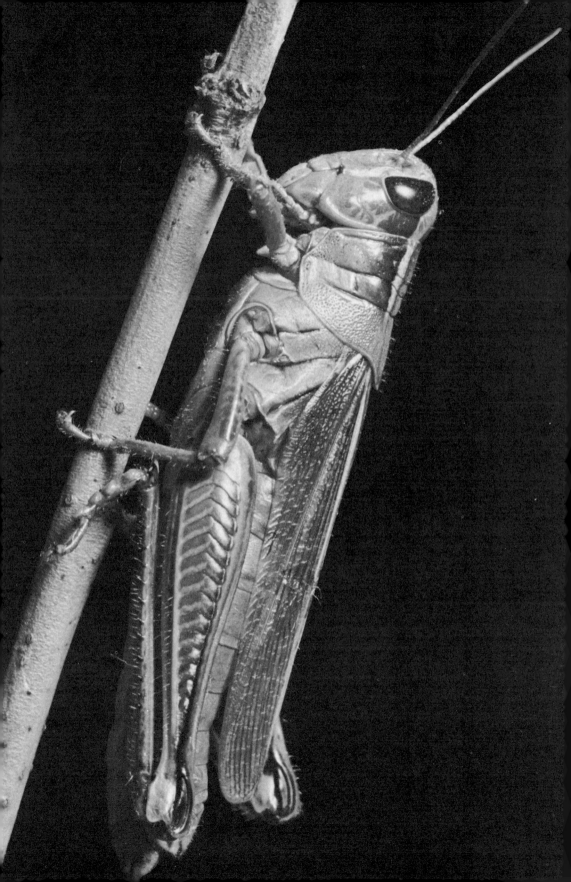

GRASSHOPPER

The grasshoppers belong to a large order of insects that also includes the katydids, cockroaches, mantids, and walkingsticks. The members of this order—Orthoptera, or *straight-winged* insects — are distinguished by two long folds in the back wings. The straight-winged insects undergo an incomplete metamorphosis. This means that the tiny insects, or nymphs, that hatch from the eggs are already similar in form to their parents, they gradually take on the appearance of the adults as they increase in size and finally develop wings. All grasshoppers and their relatives have well-developed mouthparts for biting and chewing. Except for the cicada (*see Cicada*) nearly all of the insect "musicians" are straight-winged insects.

Perhaps the best known members of the order Orthoptera are the grasshoppers. Common everywhere in fields, meadows, and gardens and along roadsides, they are famous jumpers and strong fliers. The six legs and four wings are attached to the thorax, or middle third of the body, and they are very efficient organs of locomotion. The front legs are short, the middle pair a bit longer, and the hind legs very long and strong. The muscular femur of the hind leg is nearly as long as the entire body.

The front wings are tough, membranous covers, protecting the hind, or true, wings, which are folded like a fan beneath these covers. The flight of grasshoppers is usually swift and short, but in plague years certain species fly high in the air for long distances, appearing in hordes and destroying all the vegetation in regions where they settle.

Short-horned Grasshoppers

Short-horned and long-horned grasshoppers are in two different families—one including those with antennae much shorter than the body, the short-horned grasshoppers (*Acrididae*), the other the long-horned grasshoppers (*Tettigonidae*), with threadlike antennae longer than the body, which includes the familiar katydids. One of the more familiar of the short-horned grasshoppers of dusty country roads and sandy beaches is the Carolina locust, *Dissoteira carolina,* which shows yellowish wing linings when in flight. Another of fields and roadsides is the red-legged grasshopper, *Melanoplus rubrum.* The biblical locust, which were eaten with wild honey, were short-horned grasshoppers.

Locusts, as a rule, lay their eggs in masses, underground. The female makes a hole with her ovipositor, pushes her abdomen into the hole, and deposits about 30 eggs. People walking through the fields in the autumn may see grasshoppers laying their eggs in the ground. Most species pass the winter in the egg state, and the nymphs hatch out in the spring. At first the tiny grasshopper has no wings, but during each molt it grows longer in body size and finally wings appear. By mid-summer it is full-grown. The large wings fold up like a fan. The red, or the bright yellow-and-black markings on the under surface of the wings of some species can be seen only when the insect is in flight.

Short-horned grasshoppers "sing" in various ways. Some species make a rasping sound by rubbing their hind legs against their front wings; others, while flying, rattle the hind wings against the front wings. In this family the "ears" are located on the sides of the first segment of the abdomen.

Among the many kinds of short-horned grasshoppers is the Rocky Mountain, or migratory, locust, *Melanoplus spretus,* that breeds on the high western plains in Colorado, Wyoming, Montana, and Idaho. In the years before crops were planted in these states, the Rocky Mountain locust often migrated a thousand miles to the farmlands of the Great Plains and the Mississippi Valley and caused millions of dollars in damage. Everything green was destroyed. Between 1874 and 1876 at least $200,000,000 worth of farm crops were

The short-horned grasshopper has antennae that are shorter than the length of its body

destroyed. Another, one of the most destructive of the Great Plains, is the two-striped grasshopper, *Melanoplus bivittatus*.

Long-horned Grasshoppers

The long-horned grasshoppers which include the familiar katydids, have long antennae. The males "fiddle" by rubbing a file, on the underside of one front wing, over the upper side of the other. They have hearing organs situated on the upper part of the tibiae of their front legs. The long-horned grasshoppers may be distinguished from crickets by the fact that the front wings of the former slope down on the sides while those of crickets are flat on top and bent down on the sides like a box cover (*See Cricket*).

Katydids, members of the family of long-horned grasshoppers, are beautiful insects with green, leaflike front wings. They usually live high in trees and shrubs and feed chiefly on leaves. The rasping song of the male—which sounds like *Katy did; she didn't; she did*—can be heard on dark, cloudy days as well as at night. The female has a green, sickle-shaped ovipositor at the end of the abdomen, with which she lays flat, slate-colored eggs, usually in the bark of shrubs and trees.

Other members of the long-horned grasshopper family are the meadow grasshoppers and the cricketlike grasshoppers. The former are mostly green in color, with delicate threadlike antennae. They live in fields and meadows, where they feed on plants and "sing" all day long. The latter, often called cave crickets or camel crickets, are banded with light

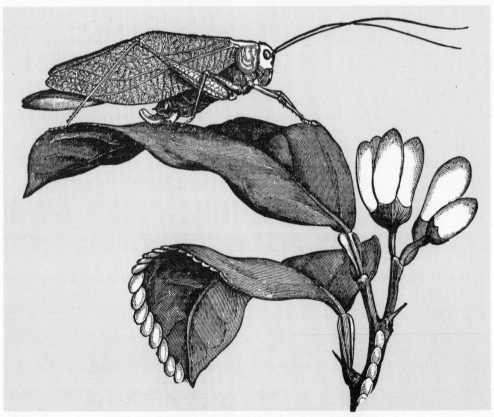

A female katydid lays her eggs on shrubs and trees

A great variety of vegetation grows in the Great Smoky Mountains

and dark brown. Some never have wings, even when adult, and thus cannot make any sound. They live in outbuildings, hollow logs, caves, and such places.

—A.K.B.

GREAT SAND DUNES NATIONAL MONUMENT

Location—South central Colorado
Size—57 square miles
Mammals—Rabbits, deer, small rodents
Birdlife—Migrating ducks visit pond at southwestern end of dunes
Plants—Sunflowers, aspens, cotton-woods, junipers, ponderosa and pinyon pines

The sands heaped up by the westerly winds along the Sangre de Cristo Mountains form the largest dunes in the United States. These dunes reach a height of almost 1,000 feet. Mount Cleveland, one of the highest snow-capped mountain peaks in the range, stands out in contrast to the rippled, brownish-gray silica dunes. Flowing from the high mountains the Mendano River skirts the dunes for some miles and finally disappears into the sands.

Accommodations—Facilities available at nearby towns
Headquarters—Within the monument—the address is Mosca, Colorado

GREAT SMOKY MOUNTAINS NATIONAL PARK

Location—Western North Carolina and eastern Tennessee
Size—720 square miles
Mammals—Black bears, foxes, raccoons, white-tailed deer, bobcats
Birdlife—Turkeys, ruffed grouse, bald eagles, vultures, many songbirds
Plants—140 native trees, including red spruces, firs, hemlocks, buckeyes, yellow birches, tulip trees; rhododendrons, mountain laurels, azaleas, dogwoods, redbuds, orchids, lilies, and violets

The Great Smoky Mountains are a part of the Appalachians. These are old mountains, formed about 19 million years ago. Most of the harsh, craggy outlines characteristic of more recent mountains, such as the Rockies, have been smoothed away by time, and even the highest peaks of the Appalachians are covered with trees. About a quarter of the Park is in virgin forest.

A number of descendants of the early settlers still live within the park, and special exhibits of early American life can be seen by the visitor to the area of the park called Cades' Cave.

Accommodations—In nearby cities and towns
Headquarters—At Gatlinburg, Tennessee

The pied-billed grebe builds its nest on a mass of floating plant debris

GREBE
Pied-billed Grebe
Other Common Names—Dabchick, dipper, hell-diver, henbill
Scientific Name—*Podilymbus podiceps*
Family—Podicipedidae (grebes)
Order—Podicipediformes
Size— Length, 12 to 15 inches
Range—British Columbia, southern Quebec, New Brunswick, and Mackenzie south to Central America, the West Indies and South America to Argentina

Small to medium-sized waterbirds, grebes have characteristics that set them apart from the apparently similar loons and ducks. They are more slender than loons, and carry their smaller heads more erect; grebes also continually shift the head from one position to another. Most of them resemble ducks with outstretched necks, but the bill is different—pointed and spearlike in most species, stubby and chickenlike in the pied-billed grebe.

Grebes are swimmers, although they do not have webbed feet. Each toe is lobed on both sides with a hornlike material, and the birds swim entirely with foot motion, keeping the wings, folded against the body. In order to take flight, grebes must run along the surface of the water while pumping furiously with their short, rounded wings.

Like loons and anhingas (*see Anhinga*), grebes are able to expel much of the air from their bodies and feathers and then sink silently beneath the water. Parent grebes often carry young birds on their backs, even when it is necessary to submerge to avoid danger. The chicks cling to the feathers during the submarine ride.

There are six species of North American grebes. Only the pied-billed grebe and the horned grebe nest east of the Great Plains, although some of the western species visit the Atlantic Coast in winter. The red-necked grebe is a bird of the prairie lakes. The western grebe and the eared grebe are accidental in the east and share a western range from British Columbia almost along the Pacific Coast. The least grebe is a tropical species that sometime nests in southern Texas and California.   —G.B.S.

Habits of the Pied-billed Grebe

Of all North American birds, grebes rank nearest to the reptiles, from which birds are thought to have evolved. Grebes are among the most primitive animal forms, yet are splendidly adapted to their way of life. Inveterate divers, they seem as well shaped for underwater travel as winged torpedoes.

At a distance they resemble ducks, but when examined near at hand, they seem more highly specialized. Their bony framework extends so far back as to afford protection to the vital organs against excessive pressure in deep water. The legs are placed far aft, their muscles being so sheathed in the skin of the body as to offer a minimum of resistance to swift movement when submerged.

Even the feet are especially adapted to underwater speed. Their flat toes have broad lobes connected with partially developed basal webs. As the foot moves forward, these webs close as with the feathering of an oar, but open in time for the back thrust. Not even the frog has more effective propulsive membranes. The thighs are muscular and enable the diver to scull itself along at a smart clip.

Of the six New World grebes, the pied-billed is the most familiar in the East. It breeds locally throughout North and South America, but many outdoorsmen note it only in the fall of the year. Grebes, or *dabchicks*, then appear here and there on our lakes and creeks, as abruptly and unaccountably as if they had dropped from the clouds. When undisturbed they float as lightly as autumn leaves and then so smoothly that the movement almost eludes the eye and scarcely ripples the placid water.

The pied-billed is the only American grebe without a crest, and is the smallest and plainest. Blackish and dark brown above, and white or silvery-ash below, its sole distinguishing field marks are the ridged, down-curved bill, a black band ringing both mandibles, and a dark throat patch. In winter plumage this band and the black on the gullet disappear. At that time the bird at a distance looks like a feathered swamp rabbit.

Despite its diminutive size the pied-billed grebe is extraordinarily vigorous. When held in the hand it can kick so incredibly fast that its feet seem to blur like the wings of a hummingbird. Owing to the awkward position of the legs, the bird is obliged to stand up like a penguin while ashore. When surprised there, a rare occurrence, it sometimes falls on its stomach and scoots toward the water, using its legs and wings simultaneously.

The short wings, used underwater whenever the creature is in a hurry, are admirably adapted to swimming underwater.

The pied-billed grebe is well equipped for its natural element in several other respects. The eyes are set forward, thus making it easier for the swimmer to see its prey under the surface without turning its head as much as do perching birds. Its stout, down-curved mandibles give it the local name of henbill on Long Island.

The pied-billed grebe's plumage is especially fitted for plunging. It is thick and satin-smooth on the underparts, but silky and hairlike on the bird's back and shoulders. So long as the pied-billed keeps its feathers preened, it never gets wet nor feels the chill of water. Such a coat slides through the liquid element as easily as the polished bottom of a racing yacht.

Another peculiarity of this plumage is that it may be quickly compressed so as to expel the air from the feathers and this enables the bird to sit low in the water when frightened. It likewise has air cells in various parts of its body, and these may be filled from the lungs or emptied at will. The grebe can float half submerged or with only its head or the tip of its bill protruding from the surface.

The escape tactics of these divers— ducking like a flash, rising only long enough to breathe, or even staying totally submerged while hastening to the shelter of shore-side weeds—are familiar to anyone who has pursued them in a boat. Being such an able diver and swimmer, the pied-billed grebe will not fly unless forced to do so or when migrating from pond to pond.

Although observers in the North seldom see a grebe take wing, it is a common sight at Wakulla Spring in Florida. This enormous fountain, 103 feet deep and 400 feet wide, is alive with many kinds of fishes, turtles, and small alligators. The pied-billed grebe is one of the familiar inhabitants of the place, where it feasts on leeches, tadpoles, frogs, insects, and small fishes. Like all its family it also swallows feathers, balls of which are often found in its stomach (*See also Limpkin*).

Watch a pied-billed grebe feeding in shoal water near Wakulla Spring and you will occasionally see it struggle in- to the air, with a frantic squawk of alarm, and flutter away just above the surface. The cause of this sudden flight is always the same—some aggressive fish or reptile has nipped its feet. In March, Wakulla Spring harbors dozens of these pretty divers, which are then courting. Chasing rivals or trying to impress their mates, they churn around in circles, tilting their heads rakishly, all the while chuckling and laughing their prolonged *cow-cow-cow-cow-cow-uh!*, a note very like that made by a swamp neighbor, the least bittern.

The love notes of the pied-billed grebe usually indicate that it is building its home, but this has nothing nestlike about it, and often escapes notice. Woven of sedges, reeds, and pondweeds, it resembles a bushel or so of half-decayed marsh vegetation. In shallow water many of these nests float, and fully three-quarters of their mass is submerged. A mere patch shows at the surface, apparently domed over, as the bird covers her eggs with nesting material whenever she leaves them.

A typical nesting site of the pied-billed grebes is a grassy, circular pond of black water, without visible inlet or outlet, in the midst of farming land 15 miles east of Poughkeepsie, New York. The lake is screened by alders, locusts, and white oaks, crowding one another to within a few paces of the margin. Then come dense growths of reeds, about shoulder-high, extending farther into the water.

The nests float in water about waist deep, 10 paces from shore, and unattached, or nearly so, to any of the withered flags standing on all sides. In this way they are free to settle when the water recedes later in the season. They resemble miniature muskrat lodges.

In a somewhat larger pond grebe nests were found floating in about four feet

Pied-billed grebe

bird, which sometimes leaves the eggs for considerable lengths of time.

Another observer once carried home three partially incubated grebe eggs and left them in a bureau drawer. A few days later he found that grebelets were pipping the shells, and so he carried them back to the pond nest.

Male and female pied-billed grebes wear identical color patterns, and share in brooding the eggs. The chicks do not remain long in their rushy cradle but paddle away with their mother, or ride on her back. When she swims through the grass it is sometimes possible to note a tiny head or two protruding from her folded wings. If she dives to escape real or imagined peril, some of the young manage to cling to her back feathers, while others are flung off.

All grebes can dive almost as soon as hatched, and by the time the swamp maples turn scarlet, they are as large as their parents and equally resourceful.

–H.M.H.

GROSBEAK
Black-headed Grosbeak
Other Common Names–Western grosbeak, black-head
Scientific Name – *Pheucticus melanocephalus*
Family–Fringillidae (grosbeaks, finches, sparrows, and buntings)
Order–Passeriformes
Size–Length, 6½ to 7½ inches
Range–Breeds from Vancouver Island, southern British Columbia, southern Saskatchewan, south to central Nebraska, California, Arizona, and east to central North Dakota, central Kansas, and western Texas. Winters in Mexico; a few linger in Louisiana

From the cottonwoods and willows along the low stream bottoms, the oaks in the canyons, and the junipers on the arid foothills, there often comes a joyous song with rising and falling passages

of water and cleverly concealed by surrounding flags and sedges. Pied-billed grebes apparently breed in small colonies, as four or five nests may be found on a pond of only a few surface acres. American bitterns nest sparingly in the same neighborhood, and a few Virginia rails. Both of these species like solitude and marshes (*See under Bittern, and under Rail*).

How does the grebe know precisely what pondweeds float best? One observer took the trouble to watch several nests long after the owners had vacated them, and they did not appear to sink. The eggs are seldom dry but may be kept slightly warmed by the fermentation of nesting material on which they lie. This lining is of softer, more feathery stuff than that of which the outside is built. It is usually warm to the touch, probably from the body of the brooding

and with round and mellow tones. It is the black-headed grosbeak's love song to his brown, sparrowlike mate. To other males it is a challenge to keep away from the thicket or grove where the nest is hidden. In fact, the best way to find its nest is to look for the source of this loud, ringing song, for often the male, taking a turn at brooding, sings right from the nest while he covers the eggs.

The black-headed grosbeak has a black head, black-and-white wings and tail, and a rusty breast. Its nest is a bulky, twig-framed structure, interwoven with stems and little sticks, and finished off with a well-woven lining of rootlets. Sometimes the nest is an old one that has been rebuilt. It is usually not more than 10 or 15 feet from the ground, but sometimes as high as 30 feet. It is most often built in oaks, willows, dogwoods, chaparrals, or other trees. The three or four eggs are a pale blue-green with dark spots.

Grosbeak means *big bill*, and the young birds have large bills like their parents, with large appetites to match. They must be fed every 10 or 15 minutes, not only while they are helpless in the nest, but for a few days after they have tried their wings.

At first they look like their mother—brown, with a light stripe over each eye. They constantly call *whe-you whe-you whe-you* as they follow their parents about, begging to be fed. This is a trying time for the parents, who must work about three times as hard as at other times of the year. In some sections scale insects constitute as much as two-fifths of the food of the black-headed grosbeaks. Beetles, too, are eaten in addition to other insects—in all, they eat about twice as much animal food as vegetable. Fruits, especially elderberries, form a minor part of their diet.

In Yosemite National Park campers call the grosbeaks butter birds, because they come down to the tables and help themselves to the butter if they are not chased away. There is nothing they like better than watermelon seeds—a slice of watermelon will keep them busy until every seed has been picked out. At summer camps in canyons, in foothills, and in the mountains, vacationers come to know these friendly birds very well.

During July the singing of the males gradually subsides. By September, just before migrating, they have not only lost their song, but their vivid black and tan coloring has lost some of its luster. They are now more brown, especially on the back. Their winters are spent mainly in the tropical forests of Mexico, often not far from the wintering grounds of the rose-breasted grosbeaks. When March comes, the two take different paths—the rose-breasted grosbeaks fly through eastern Mexico and the black-headed grosbeaks, through the western parts. They enter the United States in April, resplendent in bright new plumage and singing almost continuously.

—A.B., Jr.

The nest of the black-headed grosbeak is loosely constructed

Evening grosbeak, male (above); female (below)

Evening Grosbeak
Other Common Names—American hawfinch, sugar bird   .
Scientific Name—*Hesperiphona vespertina*
Family—Fringillidae (grosbeaks, finches, sparrows, and buntings)
Order—Passeriformes
Size—Length, eight inches
Range—Canada south to central California, northern Nevada, central Arizona and south in mountains through Mexico. Also northeastern Minnesota, northern Michigan, New York, and Massachusetts. Winters in southern California, Arizona, western Texas, Oklahoma, Arkansas, Tennessee, and South Carolina

An element of mystery has always surrounded the coming and going of these rare winter visitors whose forest home is far beyond the usual haunts of man. They are very irregular and infrequent anywhere east of the Mississippi, but now and then remarkable flights have taken place. On such occasions the extreme tameness of the birds is always very noticeable. Like its relative, the pine grosbeak, this species wanders about in flocks of varying size during the winter, visiting districts of most abundant food supply. It feeds, to a great extent, upon buds and the seeds of trees.

The song is described as a "wandering, jerky warble, beginning low, suddenly increasing in power and as suddenly ceasing as though the singer were out of breath."

The nest, known only from a few examples, is made of small twigs and rootlets and is placed low in trees or bushes. There are from three to five greenish-white eggs, spotted with brown.

Pine Grosbeak
Other Common Names—Pine bullfinch, Canadian grosbeak, American pine grosbeak
Scientific Name—*Pinicola enucleator*
Family—Fringillidae (grosbeaks, finches, sparrows, and buntings)
Order—Passeriformes
Size—Length, nine inches
Range—Northern Alaska and Canada, southern Alaska, central California, eastern central Arizona, northern New Mexico, northern New Hampshire, Maine, and Nova Scotia. In winter, southwestern New Mexico, Kentucky, and Virginia

The pine grosbeak belongs to the great evergreen forests of the north, from Maine to Alaska, although it is an erratic winter visitor throughout the northern portion of the eastern United States, coming in flocks of varying sizes. The pine grosbeak wanders widely in search of food, frequenting thickets of mountain ash and sumac, where it finds

Pine grosbeak, male (above); female (below)

abundant supplies of the diet it requires. It also feeds upon the seeds of pines and weeds.

The pine grosbeak is said to be a fearless and rather stupid bird; it is certainly easy to approach, often being caught in butterfly nets. The song is prolonged and melodious, and the call note a clear whistle.

It nests in evergreen trees a few feet from the ground. The nest is made of twigs and rootlets and is lined with fine materials. There are three or four eggs of a pale greenish-blue, spotted with brown and lilac.

Rose-breasted Grosbeak
Other Common Names—Potato-bug bird
Scientific Name—*Pheucticus ludovicianus*
Family—Fringillidae (grosbeaks, finches, sparrows, and buntings)
Order—Passeriformes

Size—Length, 7 to 8½ inches
Range—Nests from northeastern British Columbia to southern Quebec, south to Kansas, Missouri, Ohio, and New Jersey; in the Appalachian Mountains it nests as far south as northern Georgia. Winters from southern Mexico and Yucatan to Colombia, Venezuela, and Ecuador

The rose-breasted grosbeak is resplendent in its black-and-white plumage, with a triangular patch of rose-red on its breast. During the colder part of the year the rose-breasted grosbeak lives among the palms, lianas, and canes of tropical jungles in southern Mexico, Central America, and northern South America. When spring comes to the northern hemisphere, the grosbeak leaves the jungles, heads north under the cover of darkness, and, after a series of night flights, reaches its nesting range in the northern United States or southern Canada.

On a bright morning in early May, after an absence of six months, a loud, beautiful whistle indicates the rose-breasted grosbeak is back. At first there is continuous warfare between the males, which chase each other in and out of the trees, stopping only long enough between fights to pour forth a cascade of song. Their energy at this season seems almost limitless.

The males are believed to select the nesting site, usually 5 to 20 feet from the ground where some horizontal branch or crotch in a sapling forms a safe support for the nest. This might be located in a thicket or woodland close to a stream, or in an orchard. The drab female, which looks like an overgrown sparrow accepts her mate's choice. The nest is often so flimsy, that frequently the eggs can be seen from below. The three to five spotted, pale blue eggs are brooded for two weeks by both the male and the female.

In many species of birds in which the male is brightly colored, the female dull colored (sexual dichromatism), the duller, more protectively colored females

Rose-breasted grosbeak, male (above); female (below)

do all the incubating of the eggs and brooding of the chicks. The rose-breasted grosbeak, however, does not follow this rule. The male not only sits on the flimsy platform of twigs, which hardly conceals his bright throat, but even sings now and then while on the nest. A good way to find a grosbeak's nest during the month of June is to listen for the song and then to follow it to its source.

Nearly half of the rose-breasted grosbeak's food is vegetable matter, such as wild fruit.

Nesting time over, the song of the male is seldom heard until September, when, just before leaving, he bursts forth with a few soft measures, a kind of parting anthem to summer. Although most rose-breasted grosbeaks have never seen a snowflake or an icicle, they seem to anticipate the cold days ahead and leave while the weather is still warm and food plentiful. Most of them migrate south through the Mississippi valley and along the Appalachian ridges. They are not often seen in the low, flat country along the coast. —A.B., Jr.

GROUND HOG (*See under Woodchuck*)

GROUNDNUT
Other Common Names — Wild bean, potato bean, Indian potato
Scientific Name — *Apios americana*
Family — Leguminosae (pulse family)
Range — Nova Scotia to Minnesota and Colorado, south to New England, Long Island, Florida, Louisiana, and Texas
Habitat — Rich thickets
Time of Blooming — July to September

This common wild bean has been important as a food producing plant ever since the United States was settled, and even before. When the Pilgrims arrived they found the Indians using the tubers from the roots of this plant. It is said the tubers helped save the lives of many Pilgrims when other foods ran low. Both the beans and the tuberous roots are edible.

As with other members of the bean tribe, groundnuts have an ingenious way of throwing their seed. The pod curls as it dries and the curling is so rapid that the beans are thrown out.

The groundnut is a vine that trails over other plants or fences as it has no tendrils with which to climb. The stem curls about any prop it can find, thus getting itself up into the light. The pea-shaped flowers are about one-half inch long and are a beautiful rosy or brownish-purple color, with petals that look and feel like velvet.

The groundnut is a member of the pulse family whose seeds — such as beans, peas, soybeans, peanuts, and others — furnish man with enormous quantities of food. Other pulses, such as red clover, white clover, and alfalfa, furnish tons of hay for animal forage, and the roots of all aid in increasing the nitrogen content of the soil.

GROUND PINE (*See under Club Mosses and Horsetails*)

GROUND SQUIRREL
Ground squirrels are so named be-

Groundnut

cause of their terrestrial habits. North American species cover a large part of the continent from the Arctic Coast to Mexico. Being inhabitants of prairies, deserts, tundra, and open mountain slopes, they are absent from the woodland regions of the eastern parts of Canada and the United States. American forms are all comparatively small squirrels and have been divided into 31 species and 8 subgenera. These, however, can be grouped together by size and color into 12 easily recognized types.

Thirteen-lined Ground Squirrel
Other Common Names — Ground squirrel
Scientific Name — *Spermophilus tridecemlineatus*
Family — Sciuridae (squirrels)
Order — Rodentia

The camouflaging pattern on the thirteen-lined ground squirrel's back protects it from airborne enemies where cover is scarce

Size—Body length, 4½ to 6½ inches; tail, 2½ to 5¼ inches; weight, 3½ to 8 ounces

Range—Great Plains, lower peninsula of Michigan, western Ohio, western Missouri, and east-central Texas to the Gulf Coast; north to north-central Minnesota, Lake Winnipeg and central Alberta; west to northwestern Montana, western Wyoming, and eastern Arizona

This little ground squirrel's pattern of spots and stripes is not merely decoration. The prairies and grassy fields where it lives abound with sharp-eyed predators such as coyotes, badgers, weasels, snakes, and hawks. The short vegetation offers few hiding places, but the squirrel's broken pattern blends with the grass and weeds so well it is difficult to see. The ground squirrel moves cautiously, frequently standing upright to look around for enemies. If danger appears, its shrill whistle sends all neighboring ground squirrels running to their holes.

Each of their burrows has many entrances, leading to a network of tunnels, storerooms, and a nest. At night and during their five to six months' hibernation, the squirrels sleep safely underground. Litters of 6 to 12 young are born each spring. The ground squirrels' diet includes grain, berries, nuts, green plants, and insects. However, destruction of corn, wheat, and oats may make them a serious problem on farmlands where their natural predators have been eliminated.

The Townsend ground squirrel, *Spermophilus townsendi,* and its related races are rather small squirrels, uniformly smoke-gray in color and without any distinctive markings. It inhabits the dry sandy areas of the upper Sonora of the western States. It is extremely sociable and lives in large densely populated colonies.

The Washington ground squirrel, *Spermophilus washingtoni,* occurs in great abundance on the dry prairies of the Columbia River basin. This squirrel utters a soft lisping whistle much like that of the Townsend species, which it corresponds to in size and general color although its coat is flecked with small whitish spots.

Belding's ground squirrel, *Spermophilus beldingi,* frequents mountain meadows near the timberline in the Sierra Nevada. It is a small squirrel, smoke-gray in color with the back darkened with reddish-brown.

Richardson's ground squirrel, *Spermophilus richardsonii,* is a relatively large species, smoke-gray in color and dappled with buff. It frequents open prairies and flats along the Canadian border east of the Rockies.

The Columbian and Parry's ground squirrels, *Spermophilus columbianus* and *Spermophilus undulatus parryii,* live in a wide variety of habitats, ranging from the open prairies of eastern Washington to mountain peaks at 8,000 feet elevation and north to the barren lands. The Columbian squirrel is a cinnamon-buff with underparts tawny, while the Parry squirrel, the northern form, is reddish-brown flecked with rather large white spots.

The Mexican ground squirrel, *Spermophilus mexicanus,* is somewhat larger than the spotted ground squirrel, *Spermophilus spilosoma,* but both are marked with squared white spots arranged in linear lines. The Mexican race inhabits the sandy plains in both Mexico and the southern states and the range of the smaller spotted squirrel extends from Mexico to South Dakota.

The Franklin ground squirrel, *Spermophilus franklinii,* or gray gopher as it is frequently called, inhabits the prairies, pastures, and grainfields in the middle western states and adjacent parts of Canada. It is a large squirrel somewhat resembling a true squirrel with a bushy tail that is over half its total length. The

The golden-mantled ground squirrel

coarse pelage is more or less dappled.

The California ground squirrels, *Spermophilus beecheyi,* occupy the West Coast region from Lower California to Oregon. These are medium-sized squirrels, brown in color and flecked with buffy-white. Although true ground squirrels, they often climb oaks and other nut-bearing trees in search of food.

Rock squirrels, *Spermophilus variegatus,* have habits similar to other ground squirrels but show a preference for rocky canyons and rocky hillsides. These are large ground squirrels and vary from grayish-white mixed with buff to dark brown in some forms; the head and shoulders, are black and in some subspecies the entire back is black. The race inhabits the Rocky Mountain regions from Mexico to Utah.

The antelope squirrel, *Ammospermophilus,* live chiefly in the Sonoran Desert Zone. They are small squirrels, grayish-brown in color, with a narrow white longitudinal stripe on each side of the back. There are two races—one white-tailed and the other gray.

The round-tailed ground squirrels, *Spermophilus tereticaudus,* are typical desert animals living in the hottest part of the Lower Sonoran Zone in southern California and Arizona. They are similar in general to Townsend's squirrel, without any trace of dappling, but the tail is longer and less bushy, giving a round-tailed appearance.

The mantled ground squirrel, *Spermophilus lateralis,* inhabits the western mountain slopes and foothills from central Alberta and British Columbia south to Mexico. In summer pelage this squirrel has a distinct tawny or buffy mantle, covering the head and shoulders. The color pattern consists of a longitudinal white stripe on each side of the back, bordered on each side by a black stripe.
—G.G.G.

GROUPER
Red Grouper
Other Common Names—Cherna, mero, jaboncillo
Scientific Name—*Epinephelus morio*
Family—Serranidae (sea basses)
Order—Perciformes
Size—Length, 2 to 3 feet
Range—Found off the Atlantic Coast of America from Virginia to Rio de Janeiro. Very abundant off the west and south coasts of Florida

The red grouper's body is deeper and more compressed than those of the other species in its genus. Its head is large and pointed with a large mouth. The lower jaw projects beyond the upper jaw, each with two pairs of canine teeth at its front. There are two dorsal fins, the front one less than half the length of the rear one. The front dorsal is serrated and has stiff, sharp rays, while the rear dorsal has soft rays. The tail fin has a rounded rear margin.

The fish's body is olive-gray or olive-brown clouded with pale olive and blotched irregularly with grayish-white.

Red grouper

The lower part of the head and breast are usually salmon-color with some red shades. With age, the fish becomes a flushed red and its pale blotches and spots become less distinct.

The red grouper usually swims near the bottom, consuming great numbers of crustaceans and small fishes. It is not considered a good game fish, for when it is hooked it gives little or no fight. Some other groupers include the black grouper, *Mycteroperca bonaci,* the yellowfin grouper, *Mycteroperca venenosa,* and the gulf grouper, *Mycteroperca jordani.*
—M.R.

GROUSE
All grouse are plump, chickenlike vegetarians. Their flesh is esteemed by all large predators, and they are everywhere hunted by man. They are smaller than pheasants and larger than quail, though closely related to both these groups. Like them, they are ground dwellers primarily, feeding on seeds, berries, and young leaves. The species that live in wooded regions roost in trees, but all of them nest on the ground.

There are two types of breeding behavior among the grouse. The ruffed and the spruce grouse, northern birds that are found clear across the North American continent, and the blue grouse of the West, are monogamous; the male has only one mate each season, and he helps feed and care for the young. The prairie chickens, the sharp-tailed grouse, and the sage grouse, all western birds, are polygamous; each male mates with many females, but takes no part in the rearing of offspring.

The three monogamous grouse have a comparatively simple courtship. The male attracts the female by drumming, producing a deep, rolling sound by vibrating the wings. The best drummer of the three is the ruffed grouse.

The polygamous grouse go to far greater lengths. The males gather in loose flocks of up to 50 birds in the early spring to display themselves and to dance. All have air sacs on the throat which they inflate; the prairie chickens (*see under Chicken*) and the sharp-tailed grouse have feather patches on their necks which are held over their heads when they dance. The dances consist of bowing, stamping, and ruffling the feathers, with each bird making the sound peculiar to its species. The prairie chicken booms, the sharp-tailed grouse coos, and the sage grouse makes a popping noise. The few males that have asserted dominance over the others do most of the breeding with the females that gather around the dancing ground.

The ruffed grouse is a bird of the deciduous woodlands; both the blue and the spruce grouse frequent coniferous forests. The sage grouse is rarely found out of the dry, open sagebrush country. The sharp-tailed grouse prefers brushland, and seldom goes far from the thickets. Both greater and lesser prairie chickens are grassland birds. The northernmost species of grouse are the ptarmigans (*See Ptarmigan*).

Grouse are gamebirds. The game laws are designed to permit hunters to crop a percentage of them each year, but to leave enough breeding stock to replenish their numbers during the next nesting season. The current threat to the existence of some of these species is less from hunting than from the human utilization of nearly all of the former habitat. (*See Chicken: Attwater Prairie Chicken*).

—G.B.S.

Ruffed Grouse
Other Common Names—Birch partridge, drumming grouse, mountain pheasant
Scientific Name—*Bonasa umbellus*
Family—Tetraonidae (grouse and ptarmigan)
Order—Galliformes
Size—Length, 18 inches
Range—Forested areas in Central Alaska and central and southern Canada south to northern California, northeastern Oregon, central Idaho, central Utah, northwestern Wyoming, Colorado, western South Dakota, and from Minnesota and New England south to southeastern United States

Habits of the Ruffed Grouse

The drumming of the ruffed grouse is a true call of the wild. It gives voice to hemlock groves, brushy hillsides, and to alder runs. Heard occasionally at all seasons, it is primarily a spring call, just as the bark of the red fox is a winter one.

No other sound paints such pictures on the mind. At the first *thump-thump-ka-thump* rapidly accelerating into a feathered burst of sound, one sees the bold bird strut on his favorite log, head thrown back, russet crest cocked, and dark ruff glistening with iridescence. His tail is fanned, displaying the handsome, dark, terminal band, while his stout wings beat the air with infinite rapidity. They quicken to a blur almost like propellers, yet do not move his body an inch, producing a sound somewhat like the swelling exhaust of a motor.

The drumming is a love call to summon females and to challenge any males within hearing. It expresses an exuberance and determination difficult to analyze, being perhaps the most insistent come-hither sound in nature.

Hearing a cock grouse sounding off in a Connecticut forest led two ornithologists to scrutinize the terrain with con-

The ruffed grouse, unlike its relative the sage grouse, lives in forests, deep thickets, or swamps

siderable care. In addition to the surrounding stand of conifers, less than 100 acres, they saw a string of black ponds, an alder swamp, and a hardwood belt bordered by weedy fallows. Here and there runlets trickled from higher land through ferny creases, and the whole section showed a pleasing variety of contours such as grouse like to haunt.

The men saw plenty of grouse provender everywhere — scarlet wintergreen berries under the ground pine, tangles of bittersweet or greenbrier, blueberries, huckleberries, wild red raspberries, staghorn sumac holding up red candles here and there, and an abandoned apple orchard where windfalls reddened the moss. They noted occasional knee-high anthills with scratches on the sides showing where grouse had snatched their most medicinal food. No grouse could possibly starve amid such abundance. They flushed half a dozen grouse and concluded that it might be feasible to find a nest.

Under a gnarled apple tree, amid some briers, they found a former nesting site, a mere hollow perhaps a foot in diameter, strewn with broken eggshells. There were a dozen, each so neatly split open by a chick's eggtooth as to fall into symmetrical halves. They picked them up and later glued them together with wisps of surgeon's plaster. Just why the fragments had not been nibbled by white-footed mice was not clear, but as it was already late in May, the eggs may have been laid earlier that same season.

While reconnoitering the terrain around the first nest, they soon flushed a mother grouse from her home in the red pine needles. She did not rise until one of the men stepped within a few feet of her. A dozen buffy eggs, slightly smaller than a bantam's and a trifle pointed, filled the cup to the brim, or nearly so.

This grouse was a good mother, and as later observations disclosed, hatched every one. The only cover close to this nest was the branches of a white pine directly overhead, but fully 10 feet up. Nevertheless, the back of the brooding bird matched surroundings so perfectly that she might never have been seen if she had not moved. As this egg-filled cup was only a few feet from the other it was concluded that the same grouse may have made both of them. The eggs at both sites were identical in size and color. Some grouse eggs are fully ovate and faintly pinkish while others, usually unmarked, show a few faint speckles around the larger ends.

Ecologically, some 500 acres of this Connecticut terrain were in proper condition to produce a fair and continuing population of ruffed grouse. Some farming was carried on but not too intensively. The boundaries were old stone walls with a few rail fences along which grouse cover and grouse feed sprout from seeds dropped by the birds. Springs abound, and on the higher knobs and hills there was plenty of heavy cover for storm-shelter and winter refuges.

Although this type of half-wild land probably harbors a large number of nesting grouse, farms on hillsides running back to timber are liked by considerable numbers. Some grouse actually move in on such an estate, taking advantage of the owner's friendship and of the safety brought by it. An example was the place near Kent owned by Robert Nesbett, distinguished member of the National Academy of Design.

The artist found a grouse brooding her eggs at the base of a haystack close to the side door of his studio. She sat so tight that only by peering closely could one see her, eyes cocked warily. She had become so used to the Nesbetts that she never flushed when they passed the nest, although she hurtled out in a panic when a stranger arrived.

Discovery of a grouse nest may also give a glimpse of the bird's family life. In the weeds beside a brook near Scotch Plains, New Jersey, an ornithologist flushed a large hen grouse. She stormed

The male ruffed grouse produces a drumming sound by beating its wings

Ruffed grouse chicks clamber over eggs that have not yet hatched

A female ruffed grouse incubates her eggs in a nest of leaves, feathers, grasses, and roots. It is usually hidden in the litter of the forest floor

out but soon pitched and started rolling over and over, pretending to drag a broken wing in the undergrowth, and scuffling vigorously. While she was trying to lead the ornithologist away the male grouse joined her and likewise rolled and scuffed, but notably farther away. Although the ornithologist had surprised perhaps a dozen grouse families, this was the only one with which he ever saw a male bird.

The chicks, smaller than young bantams, but similarly mottled, fluttered a few feet and hid. Their wing quills had not sprouted but they could already reach cover. They squirmed into the roots of the grass, or turned up dead leaves over themselves and froze. Once hidden they remained so still that in half an hour the ornithologist could find only one, an infinitesimal chicken of the wood, with wise, limpid eyes staring up unafraid.

Once in a while an enterprising grouse takes over an old crow's nest, and lays her eggs in the deeply hollowed, moss-lined interior—a comfortable retreat but one involving great risk to the chicks. These young birds are remarkably precocious and must be difficult to restrain from tumbling over the rim and fluttering to the forest floor. Possibly the mother bird carries them earthward.

The ruffed grouse remains a mystery and a delight the year 'round. Those who try to match its cunning in the golden woods of Indian summer find it the craftiest of gamebirds and those grouse which happily survive the hunting season remain the most interesting denizens of the winter woods. Their feathers grow incredibly thick and warm, while their feet develop pectinations—comblike processes on their toes resembling miniature snowshoes—with which they skip across drifts without difficulty.

In the coldest spells ruffed grouse sometimes plunge into the deep and drifted snow and dream the night away in caverns warmed by their own bodies and breath. This is dangerous because

crust, formed by rain and sudden frosts, occasionally imprisons them. Once in a while, too, a prowling fox digs one out, but more frequently the bird escapes its pounce, hurling back a cloud of powdered snow into the pursuer's gaping mouth. In blizzards grouse are known to snuggle under the tips of hemlock branches and allow the snow to engulf them.   —H.M.H.

Sage Grouse
Other Common Names—Sage hen, sage cock, cock of the plains
Scientific Name—*Centrocercus urophasianus*
Family—Tetraonidae (grouse and ptarmigan)
Order—Galliformes
Size—Length, 28 inches
Range—Central Washington, southern Idaho, Montana, southeastern Alberta, and Saskatchewan, and western North Dakota south to eastern California, Nevada, Utah, western Colorado, and northwestern Nebraska

Habits of the Sage Grouse
Next to the wild turkey, the sage grouse is the largest gamebird and the largest of the grouse species on the North American continent. Many people believe that the sage grouse has no gizzard, because the stomach is thin-walled and soft compared with the thick, muscular gizzard of many other gamebirds and of domestic chickens. The gizzard of the sage grouse has less muscle than those of grain-eating gamebirds, but it is very similar to their structure, even to the horny, inner lining. Most gallinaceous birds — pheasants, quail, etc.—feed on grain, weed seeds, and such. They fill their gizzards, along with these palatable items, with sizable amounts of hard gravel. The gravel and grain grind together in the gizzard until both are reduced to something the rest of the bird's digestive system can handle. The sage grouse, without such a powerful gizzard, apparently gets by because

Sage grouse

anything, a barred-rock chicken that has been thoroughly rolled in dust.

Almost from the moment of its birth, the sage grouse relies greatly on the natural camouflage of its coloring for protection. Chicks are able to run about with surprising agility within minutes after hatching. In 5 to 10 days they can fly short distances but even at this stage they prefer to rely on their color for protection.

An old-timer who had spent 60 years on the high desert of central Oregon tells about the strutting.

"Dad-burndest thing you ever saw," he said. "Them old he-sage hens a puffin' and blowin' and prancin' around and makin' noises like a love-sick turtle dove."

On their strutting grounds in the sagebrush, male sage grouse show stiff white feathers on the neck as each bird turns them outward, which gives them the appearance of wearing starched white vests. Their sharp, pointed tail feathers, of which there are 20, are spread and raised, giving them the appearance of animated cactuses. When viewed from the rear the white tips of shorter feathers form a semicircular pattern against the dark of the longer pointed feathers. The wings are spread slightly and the tips brought forward and down until they touch the ground like those of some old broody hen protecting its chicks. The musical hooting of the birds seems to fill the air, and mixed with it a soft plopping sound.

On the necks of the birds are two yellowish-green air sacs. These are hardly visible until they start inflating them as part of their courtship display. With their tails spread and their wings drooping, the birds take several short prancing steps forward. At the same time, the air sacs are filled and then deflated. It is not the deflation of the air sacs that causes the plopping sound, as many people believe. It is when the cock birds suddenly contract their neck muscles, which traps air in the air sacs, causing

it confines its diet to soft foods, principally leafy plants and insects.

In most of the areas suitable for sage grouse in Oregon, the bird is scarce, though in some protected spots, such as the Hart Mountain Antelope Refuge in Oregon, large flocks can be found. Such concentrations are indications of the numbers of these birds that were formerly present over most of the Northwest.

The birds present a dark, mottled-gray appearance, although on close inspection traces of brown, black, and yellow can be observed. They resemble in color, as nearly as they resemble

As he struts within view of a female, a male sage grouse fills the two air sacs on his neck

Air sacs deflated, the male sage grouse continues to hold up the ruff of white feathers around his neck

Dance over, the male sage grouse lowers his ruff. Soon the strutting begins again and the dance is repeated

the skin of the bare air sacs to vibrate. This produces the plopping sound.

The dance of the sage grouse is a rhythmic thing to watch. The bird's little minuet is synchronized with the inflation of the air sacs. Much bobbing of the head and neck accompanies it, and at each movement of its head, the air sac seems to get larger until, at the peak, they look like two pale oranges protruding from the bird's neck. At this point the bird's head is completely hidden by its raised neck feathers.

Then the bird turns and struts in another direction. The entire "dance" lasts only a couple of seconds, but each keeps repeating it over and over.

Each male bird remains in about the same spot to do his strutting. When one male bird strays too close to another, he becomes a trespasser on the other bird's territory. The birds sidle up to within a foot of each other. Instead of standing with their heads toward each other as do domestic roosters, they are side by side, and head to tail. One moves sidewise toward the other which then dodges back out of the way. This sparring goes on for several minutes and then the defending bird sees an opening and jumps to attack. With his strong wings he gives the interloper a sound drubbing before he can get away. Fights like this occur frequently, but little damage is done other than to the loser's pride. Occasionally a bird is chased away each time it nears one of the strutting males. The next strutter in line takes up the fight until eventually the intruder, beaten and subdued, runs clear off the strutting grounds. —J.V.W.

GUANO

Guano is the dried wastes of birds, particularly that of seabirds nesting on islands off the coast of Peru. The term is also applied to the dung of bats and to fossil deposits of animal fecal matter. World headquarters of the guano industry today is off the coast of Peru, where enormously abundant small fishes (*anchovetas*) of the cool Humboldt Current in the Pacific Ocean are food supplies for millions of seabirds that nest on islands and headlands along the Peruvian coast.

Seabirds nesting in colonies—such. as the guanay, or Peruvian cormorant, consume vast quantities of these fishes each day. The excrement of the fish-eating seabirds is most often left on their island nesting grounds, where it dries and hardens in the sun. In regions where rainfall is scanty (under 40 inches a year) the material does not dissolve but accumulates as a hard brown substance with a light gray crust.

Guano is composed of uric acid, calcium phosphate, and a number of ammonium compounds, all of them readily assimilated by plants. Guano is in great demand as a fertilizer. Commercial operations have exhausted most of the known fossil guano beds (some were on islands off the coast of Florida in Pleistocene times) and most of the accumulations at existing rookeries, but some of the Peruvian guano islands are managed by the government as a continuing resource.

It has been estimated that one guanay eats about 11 ounces of anchovetas each day and deposits about 35 pounds of guano in a season on the rocks near its nest. Some 8,000 tons of guano are taken from these areas annually.

Other regions exporting guano are northern Pacific islands (dung deposits of albatrosses, terns, and boobies), Australia (from terns and gannets), Mexico (from cormorants and boobies), and western Africa (gannets, cormorants, and penguins). —G.B.S.

Recommended Reading

Bird Islands of Peru—Robert Cushman Murphy. G. P. Putnam's Sons, New York.
The World of Birds—James Fisher and Roger Tory Peterson. Doubleday, New York.

GULF STREAM

The Gulf Stream, one of many currents in the Atlantic Ocean, is a part of the sea's circulatory system. The rotation of the earth and the influence of the prevailing trade winds create the equatorial currents that move huge masses of water off Africa toward the western hemisphere in the low latitudes. These currents through the Caribbean and the Gulf of Mexico, squeeze through the Straits of Florida at a velocity of three to four knots, and move north and east across the Atlantic.

Some of this warm water surrounds Iceland and moves north along the Norwegian coast. The rest of it turns southward, bathing the western shores of Europe and North Africa and ultimately rejoining the equatorial current. It has been estimated that it takes one particle of water three years to make the entire circuit.

The influence of the Gulf Stream on the weather of Europe is considerable. The continual replenishing of warm waters by this transoceanic current gives Europe a much warmer climate than is normal for that latitude.   —G.B.S.

GULL

The most familiar seashore birds to many people are the gulls, which are often seen following ocean liners and ferry boats up and down bays or across rivers, as well as feeding along the shores at low tide. Gulls are large birds; most are larger than the crow, which they resemble somewhat in shape. Except when nesting, gulls are found along seacoasts and the larger bodies of fresh water. They have long wings that give them an easy, measured flight and that, when folded back, extend well beyond the tail. They have strong legs and fully webbed feet with which they can run rather nimbly on the shore or swim strongly on the water, where they ride higher in front and behind than a duck rides. All species when adult have white underparts and tails. In immature plumage they are variously browner and different, although the tail is always marked with black. Gulls rarely dive;

Western gull (above); California gull (below)

instead they pick up their food either on the shore or from the surface of the water.   —J.T.N.

California Gull
Other Common Names—None
Scientific Name—*Larus californicus*
Family—Laridae (gulls and terns)
Order—Charadriiformes
Size—Length, 21½ inches
Range—North central Mackenzie, south through Saskatchewan and Manitoba to Washington, Oregon, northeastern California, northwestern Nevada, and Utah (Great Salt Lake and Utah Lake), Wyoming, Montana, and eastern central South Dakota. Winters from southern Washington to the Gulf of California and Guatemala

The California gull, with its yellowish-green legs and red and black bill spot, was the famous savior of the Mormon settlers, who were threatened by a cricket invasion. Although there are multitudes of these graceful birds along the ocean beaches most of the year, they did not, as the legend would have it, come all the way from the Pacific for the sole purpose of meeting this emergency created by the cricket hordes. Many thousands of California gulls nest on the islands in Great Salt Lake, Utah.

Herring Gull
Other Common Names—Sea gull, common gull, harbor gull
Scientific Name—*Larus argentatus*
Family—Laridae (gulls and terns)
Order—Charadriiformes
Size—Length 23 to 26 inches
Range—Breeds from southern Baffin Island, Alberta, and south to eastern Long Island, New York, including the lakes near the northern edge of the United States. Winters along both coasts, and the large bodies of water inland, to the Gulf of Mexico; less common on the West Coast south of Puget Sound

On many of the rocky islands off the coast of Maine, multitudes of gulls raise their families. They are less frequently found nesting on the islands in the calm waters of the bays than on the more outlying rocks, as the islands are hardly more than low rock piles covered with a heavy growth of weeds. Each pair of gulls has its own little piece of property —just a few square feet, perhaps. But this includes a favorite standing place, usually a rock that is constantly used, a nest that is usually only a few feet away, a feeding place where the young are fed, and a hiding place, a patch of grass or weeds where the young ones hide. If a young gull strays into another family's front yard, it is attacked and sometimes killed, unless its own parents are on hand to defend it.

On the whole, however, community life is well ordered and the adults are usually quite peaceful toward their neighbors. The adults are loyal to each other and ordinarily stay mated for life. The life span of some herring gulls is known to have exceeded thirty years, and one captive pair lived more than forty-five years.

The nest of the herring gull is a loose structure built of whatever materials are nearby—chips of wood, grass, or seaweed. The three mottled brown eggs are incubated for almost four weeks by both parents, but for every hour the male spends at the task, the female puts in three. The young are brown and fuzzy, making it difficult for a person to distinguish one fuzzy baby from another.

One of the largest gull nurseries in the western hemisphere is located on the Maine coast. They also nest on many Canadian lakes and along the Atlantic, Pacific, and Arctic coasts of Canada, and on many islands of the Great Lakes, with the exception of Lake Erie. Recently, small nesting colonies have been found in Viriginia, farther south than they had ever been recorded.

The common, dusky brown gulls that are seen in such numbers are still young birds, and it is not until the end of their fourth year that they are fully adult.

The herring gull is between 23 and 26 inches long, and is the commonest gull in most parts of the East. The similar California gull is one of the commoner western species. The herring gull occurs in great numbers around some of the coastal cities such as Boston, New York, and Philadelphia, and is common at times around Seattle, Washington. Inland, it is numerous during migration, and in winter around the waterfronts of Toronto, Buffalo, Cleveland, Chicago, St. Louis, and many other cities. Large cities always offer a bountiful food supply, since gulls are scavengers and will eat almost anything. They are attracted by sewage, garbage dumps, and refuse thrown from boats.

Gulls have one curious habit that may

*Ring-billed gulls (above)—adult (left), immature (right); herring gulls (middle)—
adult (below), immature (above); laughing gulls (below)—immature (below), winter
adult (middle), summer adult (above)*

be noticed time and again—that of picking up a clam or mussel, rising 40 or 50 feet with it, and letting it fall. If the hard shell does not break, the bird tries again until it succeeds.

Gulls add a great deal of charm to the seashore, and much would be lost with their disappearance. Their graceful soaring, wheeling, and dipping accentuate the movement of the waves, making them a pleasure to watch. Some people object to their fish-eating habits, but no fish-eating bird is really harmful to man's interests. Under natural, wild conditions their presence is favorable to all forms of life in lakes and seas, for they play a vital part in the check-and-balance drama of nature.   —A.B., Jr.

Laughing Gull
Other Common Names—Black-headed gull
Scientific Name—*Larus atricilla*
Family—Laridae (gulls and terns)
Order—Charadriiformes
Size—Length, 16½ inches
Range—From New England and Nova Scotia south along Atlantic Coast and Gulf Coast to Texas and the Salton Sea in southeastern California; also, the Bahamas, Greater and Lesser Antilles, and northern Yucatan. Winters from the Pacific Coast of Mexico to Ecuador and northern Peru, and from the Gulf of Mexico south to West Indies and Brazil

The laughing gull is the largest of the black-headed gulls of North America; it is not likely to be confused with any other member of the family in the eastern United States except perhaps the Bonaparte's gull. Adults of the latter species, however, have a black bill, a much lighter colored back, and outer primaries that are mainly white with black tips. The laughing gull has outer primaries of black.

These beautiful and interesting gulls were formerly very abundant in favored localities along the eastern and southern coast of the United States, but during the latter part of the last century they

were killed in large numbers to supply the millinery trade. Few experiences are more interesting than to visit a nesting colony of these birds in the salt meadows. At earliest break of day the air is full of a strange medley of voices, which —coming out of the gray and misty dawn and floating across the marsh's wide expanse—might well simulate weird, human, ironic laughter.

The nest, when in marshes, consists of grasses or seaweed built up into a considerable pile; when on bare islands, it is sometimes a mere hollow in the sand, without concealment. There are from two to five eggs (usually three), olive-gray and spotted with black.

Western Gull
Other Common Names—Sea gull
Scientific Name—*Larus occidentalis*
Family—Laridae (gulls and terns)
Order—Charadriiformes
Size—Length, 24 inches
Range—Northern Washington south along Pacific Coast to Baja California and Gulf of California to Sonora

The western gull is the darkest of the large gulls of the Pacific Coast. The smaller Heermann's gull, *Larus heermanni*, is darker, but does not have the white trailing edge on the wings of adults. Western gulls are seldom found inland; they inhabit the outer islands, along the coasts of Oregon and California. During the winter, they are often seen around refuse dumps and harbors where fishing industries are located. They also follow ships, eating discarded garbage. Their major foods, however, are clams, crabs, shrimp, and fishes.

The nests of western gulls are built in loose colonies on the tops or slopes of offshore islands or occasionally on remote sea cliffs or headlands. They often are found among colonies of murres and cormorants whose eggs and young are eaten if the nests are left unguarded. Two to four buff or olive colored eggs with brown patches are laid in a nest of dried grasses. The nest has a shallow depression at the top and is built on the ground on a low mound.

Ring-billed Gull

Frequently misidentified because they are so like the herring gull, the ring-billed gull, *Larus delawarensis*, is decidedly smaller and its head and bill are also relatively smaller. When the two species are standing together the difference in size is conspicuous. When on the water together, the relative difference in size of head and bill is readily appreciable. On the wing, or not associated, they are surprisingly difficult to differentiate. The adult plumage is practically identical with that of the herring gull; bill is yellowish-green at base with a complete black cross band and a whitish tip, perfectly diagnostic if the greenish base and whitish tip are noted. (Other species sometimes have banded bills when subadult.) Legs and feet greenish, unlike the flesh-colored feet of the herring gull. The color of the feet can be made out at a considerable distance as a gull swoops down to pick something from the water. Its immature first year upper parts are mottled gray; lower parts are white, more or less mottled with gray; tail is white with a narrow black band; its legs and feet, flesh color. The colors of the young ring-billed gull are identifiable, but easily confused with those of an intermediate herring gull by a careless observer or one not familiar with both birds. That of the ring-billed is less irregular and variable, more evenly spotted, and in the stage where the herring gull is equally light-colored it shows a certain amount of the clear pearl-gray of the adult on upper parts. In stooping to pick up food the ring-billed flutters more than the herring gull does; it is a less noisy bird with a hoarser, lower pitched voice. The ring-billed gull is common in fall along coasts and bays in larger flocks of the herring gulls. On the more sheltered waters it is seen frequently throughout the winter in small groups of its own species. Uncommon elsewhere, it arrives from the north in August.

Great Black-backed Gull

The black-backed gull, *Larus marinus*, the largest of the various species, is decidedly larger than a herring gull and, not only seems to, but actually does flap its wings more slowly. Thus, sometimes, it may be picked out in flight at great distances. In ordinary flight, the herring, ring-billed, and laughing gulls have about six flaps to two seconds and the black-backed gulls about five — not a great difference but one easily checked with a watch. The adult is like a herring gull but its gray mantle is replaced by almost dead black. In a good light this dark mantle shows through even from below. The immature first-year plumage is much whiter than a herring gull's and is about the tone of an immature ring-billed gull, but the much larger size of the black-backed gull will differentiate it at once. It is less variable and more sharply and evenly spotted than an intermediate herring gull, from which it is differentiated with difficulty. Older birds of this species become darker and blacker above as the herring gull becomes paler and grayer. The black-backed gull's voice is like that of the herring gull in form but deeper, hoarser, and less ringing. Common along the coast in winter, it is loosely associated with the herring gull. When associated with large flocks of the latter, the proportion is not more than 25 to 1,000. Where gulls are less abundant the proportion may be greater.

Bonaparte's gull

Bonaparte's gull *Larus philadelphia*, is decidedly smaller than any other gull of regular occurrence, with a more tern-like, often fluttering flight. The long flight feathers (primaries) are largely white, surrounded by a narrow black margin at the end of the wing. In flight this gives the appearance of a length-

Fuzzy young herring gulls stick close to their parents. If they wander into another gull's territory they might be killed

wise patch or stripe of white, diagnostic of this species in any plumage. The adult has a pearl-gray mantle, a black head in summer, a white one in winter with a gray patch on the auricular region. The immature first year has upper parts somewhat mottled and margined, and a narrow black band on tail, but underparts are unmarked white; head is much like the winter adult. The Bonaparte's gull is usually silent, but sometimes has a harsh, ternlike note. Common in flocks on the harbor, sound, or over the ocean in spring, late fall, or early winter; uncommon on bays or inland waters; casual only in midsummer and midwinter.

Uncommon Species

The glaucous gull, *Larus hyperboreus,* and Iceland gull, *Larus glaucoides,* occasional in winter, resemble the herring gull but have the ends of the wings fading to white instead of being black. In first year plumage they are mottled brownish-gray, paler in tone than a herring gull, with the primaries paler instead of black; in intermediate plumage they are sometimes almost completely white. The glaucous gull is larger than a herring gull with a relatively larger, heavier bill; the Iceland gull is the same size as a herring gull or a trifle smaller, with a relatively smaller bill. The kittiwake gull is common well out to sea in winter, but is rarely seen on the coast.   —J.T.N.

GUM
Sweet Gum

Other Common Names—Liquidambar, red gum, bilsted, star maple, satin walnut

Scientific Name—*Liquidambar styraciflua*

Family—Hamamelidaceae (witch-hazel family)

Range—Native from southwestern Connecticut and extreme southern New York, west to southern Missouri and eastern Texas, south to central Florida

Habitat—Will grow in moderately dry situations, but favors rich level land subject to occasional flooding

Leaves—Basically five-lobed and star-shaped but with many variations. Four to seven inches long with small, rounded "teeth" on all edges and a rather long stem

Bark—When young, light gray with many spots and speckles, becoming gradually rougher and darker; when old, splitting and deeply furrowed, then brown, flecked with light gray

Flower—Two to three inches; upright, green clusters of hairy blossoms on the ends of twigs. From March to May, according to climate

Fruit—Seed balls 1 to 1½ inches across, with many horny points opening to release hundreds of grainlike seeds

A number of trees are commonly called gum trees after the substances they exude. In Australia, for instance, the eucalyptus tree is known as the gum tree; in parts of the United States there are the so-called black gums, including the tupelo (*See Eucalyptus, and Tupelo*). There are also the sweet gums, represented by four species. Two are native to Asia, one to South America, and one to the eastern United States, particularly in the South where it often forms nearly pure forest stands in bottomlands. Mature trees are straight-trunked and attain heights of 50 to 75 feet; some trees may reach a height of 150 feet. Younger trees are pyramidal in shape, with a pagodalike crown. In the northern part of its range, the sweet gum is more localized in its distribution, favoring the edges of streams or moist, mountainous areas.

The prickly seed balls that litter the ground in great numbers are a source of food for eastern chipmunks and gray squirrels as well as for a variety of birds such as mallard ducks, quails, bob-whites, Carolina chickadees, purple finches, eastern gold finches, juncos, towhees, and Carolina wrens. In the southeastern United States its wood

Sweet gum

forms 10 to 25 percent of the beaver's diet.

No other North American tree has such characteristic star-shaped, five pointed leaves, although these often vary in general appearance. In autumn these leaves turn many shades of yellow, orange, crimson, and maroon. The twigs have little corky winglike projections that, along with the leaves, serve to identify the sweet gum.

Sweet gum wood, which weighs about 37 pounds per cubic foot, is valuable for making boxes and crates, as well as furniture and interior finishes. It is often used as a substitute for Circassian walnut because of its similar grain patterns.
—G.A.B.

GUNNISON NATIONAL MONUMENT (*See under Black Canyon*)

GYPSY MOTH (*See under Insect: Insect Control*)

GYRFALCON (*See under Falcon*)

HABITAT (*See Animal: Animal Habitats of a Forest*)

HAIL

Ice formed high in the air and falling to earth is called hail. Usually occurring in the advance wave of severe thunderstorms, hailstones begin their careers as raindrops. Rain is moisture condensing out of the atmosphere and plunging toward the ground. Strong updrafts catch the rain, hurling it high into the cold upper air, where it freezes. As it falls once more, it acquires additional moisture; but it is again hurled aloft, where it again freezes and increases in size. This process may be repeated again and again, until the hailstones become too heavy for the play of the updrafts, and they fall through the clouds to the earth below.

Hailstones cause great damage to crops, to wildlife, and to man-made structures. One of the largest hailstones recorded in the United States fell near Potter, Nebraska, in July, 1928; it measured 17 inches in circumference, and weighed 1½ pounds. Hailstones possibly three times as large have been reported from Spain, Germany, and India.

—G.B.S.

Effects of Hail on Waterfowl

Across the North American continent, many forces, both man-made and natural, annually reduce waterfowl populations. Man is usually considered to be the greatest single factor accounting for the yearly reduction of waterfowl, either through hunting or by the destruction or modification of waterfowl habitat. It is a difficult task to evaluate man's role in this problem because of the many interrelated factors inherent in the ecology of any wildlife species. If, however, one sets aside human influences and considers only the natural causes of waterfowl population reduction, one is frequently able to measure their force more accurately. This is especially true when something like disease, oil pollution, or hail strikes a limited area with a known waterfowl population.

For centuries, hailstorms have swept across areas of thunderstorm activity on the North American continent. Fortunately for all concerned, these storms frequently dissipate before extending over too great an area, or they are not severe enough or in the right locations to cause heavy property damage. On the prairies of the North American midcontinent, damage is usually confined to the flattening of gardens and grain crops or the destruction of greenhouses. Occasionally very severe storms do occur, accompanied by high winds and hailstones of very destructive size. Assessments of damage caused by these storms are customarily made in reference to the destruction of man's real and personal property. Seldom has it been possible to make observations of the effects of these storms on our wildlife resources.

Since 1947 the Bureau of Sport Fisheries and Wildlife of the United States Fish and Wildlife Service in cooperation with the Canadian Wildlife Service and the respective Provincial Game Branches have been conducting annual surveys of the important waterfowl breeding grounds of Canada. These surveys are conducted by trained biologists who act as both aerial and ground crews. The population and production data which these crews gather provide invaluable information needed by the federal governments of Canada, the United States, and Mexico in the management of waterfowl resources.

Alberta is one of the Canadian provinces so surveyed each year. It also happens that this province, because of the proximity of the Rocky Mountains to its prairies, has a greater incidence of hailstorms than does any other Canadian waterfowl-producing area. This fact, plus the presence of the waterfowl survey teams resident in the field from May 1 to August 1, provides an excellent opportunity for a study of the effects of hailstorms on waterfowl.

Atmospheric conditions change radically from month to month, and from day to day. Some years are nearly hail free, whereas others, such as 1953 and 1954, are classed as "hail years." Two storms, one on July 14, 1953, and another on July 18 of the same year, were particularly severe and widespread. The area covered by each storm had been censused to obtain waterfowl population indices, and the earlier of the two storms obliged further surveys by crossing one of the intensive ground study areas, where a detailed investigation had been made which included an accurate census of all waterfowl, by species, sex, and age (adult or juvenile). More perfect conditions for the study of the effects of hailstorms on waterfowl populations could hardly have been devised.

Shortly after noon on July 14, 1953, an extremely severe hailstorm originating a few miles southwest of Delburne, Alberta, beat a path northeasterly to the North Saskatchewan River, 140 miles away. The most destructive path of this storm, where damage to crops was judged by the Hail Insurance Board to be 100 percent, was 5 miles in width. Reaching 140 miles in length, it left 700 square miles of nearly total destruction. The storm was accompanied by winds which at times reached 75 miles per hour, and it deposited hailstones slightly larger than golf balls. The damage caused by such natural phenomenon, in flattened grain crops, mangled trees, battered buildings, and the losses of livestock and wildlife, is severe.

From the air the track of this hailstorm could be seen for miles. Within 48 hours after the storm the sun had bleached the shredded vegetation. A golden-yellow band, extending to the horizon, marked the path of the storm. The emerald-green of growing wheat and aspen bluffs, outside the storm area, provided a colorful contrast to the yellowing plant debris.

A close investigation of the hail damage on the ground presented a picture of unbelievable devastation. Grasses and herbs were shredded beyond recognition and beaten into the earth. Trees and shrubs were stripped of all leaves and small branches and the bark on one side of the larger trees had been torn away or deeply gouged by hailstones. Plants growing in waters of the potholes and lakes were reduced to pulp. Emergent vegetation had disappeared, destroyed and beaten under the water's surface by the weight of the hail. Ponds that had been choked with grasses, sedges, cattails, and bulrushes since June, were stripped of all evidence of former plant growth. The waters of these ponds became extremely turbid as a result of the violent flailing action of the hail upon shallow water. Songbirds, hawks, owls, crows, grouse, coots, grebes, ducks, and geese were wiped out impartially. In fact, every exposed bird and small mammal was killed in a matter of minutes. Adult ducks of all species, divers and puddlers, as well as their young, littered the surfaces of the potholes and lakes in the path of this storm. By the following day, waterfowl lay in rows on the shores of the ponds, entangled in the plant debris which had been swept ashore by the wind.

When hailstorms of moderate intensity strike a pothole with dense edge and emergent vegetation, waterfowl can usually find sufficient cover to escape serious harm. But in this storm, even lush, five-foot stands of cattails were reduced to battered stubs. In one such cattail stand, well hidden under the live and dead stems of these plants, was a scaup nest containing eggs which were to have hatched in about 48 hours. After the storm, no upright vegetation remained, and, though the nest was covered by the female when she left, hail had beaten down the surrounding plant growth, exposing the eggs and destroying them. The well-incubated eggs were shattered and crushed, exposing the mutilated, fully-developed duck embryos that were near hatching.

Many ducks, both adults and young, were examined after the storm in order to learn the physical effects of the hail on the bodies of these birds. Death was caused by a crushing of the skulls and massive contusions on the backs of all those examined (See under Longspur: Lapland Longspur, Bird of Tragedy).

One interesting but gory aspect of these dead birds was the fact that, repeatedly, one found the upper mandible torn from the adult ducks, leaving only the lower mandible and the exposed tongue. Apparently, when ducks were struck on the head, crushing the skull and tearing away the upper mandible, death was instantaneous and other contusions were of minor nature, possibly because of the limp attitude of the duck. However, if the blows came on the back before they occurred on the head, injury to the body was more severe. It is possible that death caused by severe blows on the back would cause a duck to drop its head into the water, thus protecting the head from further harm. This is perhaps a minor point, but damage to all dead birds, adult and juvenile, seems to have been of either one type or another, but usually not both. Only an occasional bird was found with a broken wing, which may indicate that the severity of the storm was too great to allow them to try to escape by flying. The fact that the storm occurred during the period of adult molting meant that many adults as well as most young were not well protected by feathers. Thus, birds were

frequently found that had been scalped and had the skin torn from their backs.

Of even greater interest—other than the actual physical effects of hail on ducks—were the overall effects of these storms on known waterfowl populations. The aerial "highways" that were flown by investigators above the area of the July 14, 1953 storm to measure waterfowl populations crossed the storm's path at 10 different locations. These courses are flown twice each summer, once in May to census waterfowl breeding populations, and again in July to measure their production. From these aerial surveys in 1953 it was possible to measure the total loss of waterfowl from one hailstorm. In May these aerial surveys produced a waterfowl population index for the parklands of 16.4 pairs or 32.8 ducks per square mile. Therefore, in May 1953 a minimum of 11,500 pairs or 23,000 ducks were resident within the area devastated by hail on July 14. When the second aerial survey was conducted early in July, the same area netted a brood index of 3.3 broods per square mile with an average of 5.7 ducklings per brood. Thus, at least 2,310 broods, or an additional population of about 13,190 ducklings, was present at the time of the storm. If we add the adults in May (23,000) to the young in July (13,190), the total loss is some 36,190 waterfowl. This is exclusive of coots which are also a very plentiful species in Alberta's parklands (See under Coot).

The figure of 36,000 is thought to represent a minimum loss figure for this single storm for several reasons. First, the storm's path, though it was seldom less than five miles wide, was frequently wider than that. Second, it is a well-known fact that visibility factors reduce accuracy of observation in the parklands by an appreciable degree. Actual populations are known to be as much as twice the index figure obtained by an aerial census of ducks in the parklands. Third, in July a great proportion of all male ducks usually leave their females and assemble in large lakes in molting concentrations, leaving only the females with the broods. Though this ordinarily removes half of the adult population, several very important molting areas happened to be in the path of this storm—lakes such as Buffalo, Wavy, Thomas, and scores of others too small to be named but too large to be classed as potholes. Thus all ages and species and both sexes of waterfowl were destroyed with impartiality. It is felt, therefore, that the estimate of 36,000 dead ducks resulting from this single storm is very conservative.

Though no effort will be made to describe the second severe storm which struck the central prairies on July 18, 1953, it was again possible to assess the damage caused by it. In this case, within an area of 260 square miles, some 23,000 adults and 4,000 young ducks were destroyed. Thus, in less than a week, a minimum of 60,000 ducks were killed by two storms in one segment of the North American continent's best waterfowl-producing habitat.

However, 1953 and 1954 were both classed as severe hail years, and scores of storms occurred in both years whose paths were never plotted except by the Insurance Board. Based on their charts, however, and the factors limiting visibility on aerial surveys, it is likely that some 150,000 ducks were lost by hailstorms in the Province of Alberta in 1953 alone, and nearly as many more may have been lost the following year. Taking the factor of limited visibility into account, these losses may have been as high as 250,000 in both 1953 and 1954.

Aside from periodic outbreaks of botulism in some of our western waterfowl concentration areas, few other observed natural forces cause the loss of so many waterfowl in any one season (See Botulism). Even this powerful natural force may be tamed in the future, since much time and money are being expended in Alberta and in other western areas in

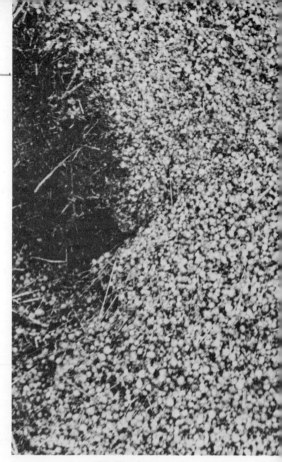

Hailstones

attempts to modify these devastating storms. Present efforts are directed toward changing the hail to rain or "soft" hail by seeding clouds with carbon dioxide ice or silver iodide from an aircraft, seeding with silver iodide generators on the ground, or seeding by projectiles shot into the clouds where chemicals are then released. Tremendous changes have been noted by farmers whose crops are located in major hail paths when cloud seeding has been practiced. Knowledge of the paths of these storms, the areas and conditions which give birth to them, and the incidence of their frequency is paying dividends. Continuance of these experiments may save millions of dollars worth of property as well as hundreds of thousands of songbirds, waterfowl, and small mammals. Since hailstorms are common throughout so much of North America, scientific efforts to tame this destroyer will save inestimable numbers of birds and mammals. —A.G.S.

HAKE (*See under Fish*)

HALIBUT
Atlantic Halibut
Other Common Names — None
Scientific Name — *Hippoglossus hippoglossus*
Family — Pleuronectidae (righteye flounders)
Order — Pleuronectiformes
Size — Length, five to nine feet
Range — Northern and subarctic Atlantic. Strays as far south as New Jersey and New York

The halibut is related to the flounder and is similarly shaped, being flat with a top and a bottom side (*See under Flounder*). The Atlantic halibut is narrower than most flatfish — about one-third as broad as it is long — but is very thick from top to bottom. It usually weighs about 100 pounds, but specimens up to 700 pounds have been taken.

Its mouth cuts back as far as its eyes and has sharp curved teeth. Its dorsal fin has 98 to 105 rays; it starts over the eye and runs to the base of the tail and is at its highest at the center. The anal fin has 73 to 79 rays and runs from behind the pectoral fins to the base of the tail.

The upper side of the halibut is olive, chocolate-brown, or slate-brown. The lower side is either pure white or white clouded with gray.

The halibut spends most of its time on the bottom, feeding voraciously on other fishes. It is an important food fish and is popular with game fishermen.

Other halibuts are the Pacific halibut, *Hippoglossus stenolepis*, and the Greenland halibut, *Reinhardtius hippoglossoides*. Both are considerably smaller than the Atlantic halibut.   — M.R.

HARE
Many people naturally confuse hares with rabbits, not realizing that they are scientifically classed as different animals. The difficulty is compounded by the fact that several true hares are called jackrabbits and some true rabbits are called hares. The name rabbit should be applied only to the cottontails, the genus *Sylvilagus* (*See Rabbit*).

Hares, the genus *Lepus*, have longer ears and longer hind legs than rabbits and their digestive tracts differ in structure. When hares are born, their eyes are open and their bodies are well covered with fur; rabbits are born without fur and have their eyes closed for a week or more after they are born. Hares also tend to be larger than rabbits.

There are 11 species of hares in North America and Mexico. One of these is the European hare, *Lepus europaeus*; first introduced into North America late in the 19th Century, it has spread across eastern United States and around the Great Lakes.

Three species of hares found in the United States are generally grouped as black-tailed jackrabbits, although only a part of the upper surface of their tails is actually black. These three are the black-tailed jackrabbit, *Lepus californicus*, Gaillard's jackrabbit, *Lepus gaillard*, and the antelope jackrabbit, *Lepus alleni*. The two latter species are found in small areas of Mexico, Arizona, and New Mexico. A close relative of *Lepus californicus*, the black jackrabbit, *Lepus insularis*, is known only on Espiritu Santo Island in the Gulf of California.

Jackrabbits have gained their common names from their long ears, which people associated with jackasses. While

Halibut

D.BERRY

The black-tailed jackrabbit is a lanky mammal that can outdistance all but the swiftest of its natural predators

running, the jackrabbit periodically makes great leaps, or "spy hops," as if to check on the pursuer. Leaps as long as 15 to 20 feet have been recorded, but these are not usual.

Hares of the Arctic Tundra

There are two closely related species of large hares that live only in the North American Arctic. The Alaskan hare, *Lepus othus*, lives on the Alaskan tundra from the vicinity of the mouth of the Colville River on the north coast all the way around the west coast to the Gulf of Alaska at the base of the Alaska Peninsula. The other species, the arctic hare, *Lepus arcticus*, lives on the tundra from near the mouth of the Mackenzie River all the way to Newfoundland and as far north as Cape Morris Jesup in Greenland. The more familiar snowshoe hare, *Lepus americanus*, has a range that extends across North America from Alaska to Labrador, down the West Coast, through the Rockies and throughout northern and northeastern United States.

Compared with the common snowshoe hare, which weighs from 2 to 5 pounds, the tundra hares are extremely large, usually ranging in weight from 5 to 10 pounds. A veritable monster of 16 pounds was once captured near Nome, Alaska. Tundra hares are heavily furred, even on the soles of their feet. In winter they are pure white except for the tips of the ears, which are black. The summer pelage varies from shades of gray in the eastern Arctic to cinnamon brown or dark brown in the Alaskan hares. The trend toward darker brown continued in the tundra hares, *Lepus tschukschorum*, of northern Siberia. All the tundra hares change into the dark summer pelage except those on Elles-mere Island and those of Greenland, which remain white all the year, show-ing only a faint dusky wash on the back in summer.

The upper incisor teeth of these far northern hares are elongated and pro-jecting. This evolutionary feature has been explained as an adaptation for picking bits of vegetation from hard snow, but it also helps the hares to graze on crustose lichens on rocks. Tun-dra hares are usually seen in rocky places scraping crustose lichens from the rocks with their teeth.

The size of the home range of the tundra hares is not known, but with the food supply on the tundra not as concen-trated as in the forested regions, these hares probably cover a larger area in their feeding than do their relatives, the hares that live in the taiga of Siberia. Each hare has several resting places, or *forms,* usually situated along-side large rocks on a hill or a ridge top. From this position the hare can watch for danger; on the other hand, it can also be seen from a great distance when its coat color contrasts with its sur-roundings. From these forms, the hares travel to lichen-covered rocks, sedge and grass lowlands, mats of dwarf birch, or clumps of willow to feed. They return to their forms to loaf, groom their fur, and sleep.

The tundra hares appear to breed in April and May and have their young in late June or early July. Four to eight (usually seven) young are born in a lit-ter. When born they are fully furred and have their eyes open. The young huddle together for warmth and comfort, since the mother only visits the nest to nurse them. The nest, constructed of dry grasses and sedges, is usually in a sheltered hollow among rocks. While most arctic hares live rather solitary lives, those inhabiting the far northern islands of the Canadian Arctic Archi-pelago sometimes may be seen in regular herds numbering up to a hundred. The hares of Ellesmere Island and Greenland sometimes exhibit what is among the most remarkable sights in North Ameri-can natural history. When one of the hare herds is frightened, the animals rise on their hind legs, hold their fore-legs pressed tightly against their bodies, and then dance about until the source of danger is located, at which time they all bound away kangaroo fashion.

Below the Arctic, in the temperate regions, hares, along with rabbits, make one of the basic links in the ecological food chain of other animals. They are the primary producers of animal protein, turning the plants they eat into a form of stored energy that is usable by other animals—the carnivorous foxes, weasels, and the birds of prey (*See under Food Chain*). This is equally true in the high Arctic, where the large arctic hares, along with the barren ground caribou, act as protein producers for the arctic fox, the tundra wolf, the snowy owl, and the gyrfalcon. The tundra hares are important to the Eskimo not only as a source of food but as a source of a very warm, although not very durable, fur that they use for socks and mitten liners. When cut into strips, rolled, and then woven the fur of the tundra hares makes one of the warmest blankets known.

In areas where tundra hares have never been molested by man they are trusting and easy to approach, but wher-ever they have been hunted they become extremely wary.   —W.O.P., Jr.

Black-tailed Jackrabbit

Other Common Names—Narrow-gauge mules, small mules, hare
Scientific Name—*Lepus californicus*
Family—Leporidae (hares and rabbits)
Order—Lagomorpha
Size—Body length, 19 to 24 inches; weight, 4 to 7½ pounds
Range—West Coast from Oregon down through Baja California, eastward through Southwest and Mexico into Mis-souri and Iowa

The lanky black-tailed jackrabbits are among the more familiar residents of the open areas and grasslands of the West. Good eyesight and keen hearing warn these jackrabbits of approaching danger, and with their long legs they can outdistance all but the swiftest enemies.

The black-tailed jackrabbit does not seek shelter to make its home but settles for a scratched-out hollow barely hidden by weeds or brush. The young are born in this shallow, open burrow. Usually two or three to a litter, they are well furred and their eyes are open at birth — one of the features that marks them as hares. The jackrabbit young are soon able to care for themselves, leaving their mother free to start raising another litter.

At times black-tailed jackrabbits become extremely abundant. Since their diet consists of grasses, alfalfa, and grain they can, when too numerous, do tremendous damage to crops. In areas where coyotes and other predators have not been eliminated, however, these natural enemies of the jackrabbit usually keep the population under control.

HARRIER (*See under Hawk: Marsh Hawk*)

HARVESTMEN(*See Daddy-long-legs*)

HAWK

The hawks and their allies are classed together in the order Falconiformes, that of daytime hunters, diurnal birds of prey. While certain other species, such as skuas, jaegers, the kea, jays, and shrikes are partly or largely day-hunting flesh-eaters, only the Falconiformes and the owls are adapted wholly to a meat diet.

The order has five families and a number of subfamilies. The American vultures, of the family Cathartidae, include five species of carrion eaters, three of which occur north of Mexico. They are better at soaring, utilizing wind currents for lift and for distance flight, than any other landbirds. The talons and beaks of these species are not as powerful as those of the other Falconiformes, and vultures do not ordinarily attack living animals (*See Condor and under Vulture*).

The secretary bird of Africa, a slim, longtailed snake killer, is in one family all by itself, the family Sagittariidae. So, too, is the osprey (family Pandionidae); a fish-eater. The osprey has two opposable toes on each foot, and the toe pads have spines that help it in clutching fishes.

The falcons, of the family Falconidae, are the fastest flying hawks, and their bodies suggest speed. The wings are long and pointed, and the general effect is one of streamlined efficiency. In this family the birds have a notch in each side of the lower edge of the upper mandible, a distinctive characteristic (*See under Falcon*). The caracara of Mexico and the southeast is a most unusual member of this group. It scavenges on the ground, whereas the others swoop down on flying birds or attack other small animals from above (*See Caracara*).

The largest family of hawks is the family Accipitridae. It contains the Old World vultures, the kites, the true hawks, the eagles, and the harriers. These birds are placed in the same family because of internal structural similarities, although externally these resemblances are often not apparent.

Of the nine subfamilies in the Accipitridae, three, including the Old World vultures and the serpent eagles, do not occur in North America. Three subfamilies of small hawks are kites, graceful birds that feed mostly on insects. In North America subfamily Accipitrinae contains accipiters, the three bird hawks: the goshawks, the Cooper's hawk, and the sharpshinned hawk. These are noted for their short, round-tipped wings, and long tails, and small heads (*See under Accipiter*).

The largest subfamily of hawks is the Buteoninae, the buteos, which includes the eagles and the chunky, broadwinged, broadtailed rodent hawks, such as the red-shouldered, red-tailed, and many others (*See under Buteo*). The last subfamily, Circinae, is that of the harriers. The only harrier in North America is the marsh hawk, a slender bird with wings that are long and somewhat rounded, a long, narrow tail, and a distinct white rump patch. In this species, the female is brown, the male gray. The birds feed on small mammals and amphibians.

Hawks were once persecuted relentlessly. Some of them do prey on gamebirds, and hunters resent what appears to them to be competition. It is only in the past fifty years or so that an understanding has come of the function of hawks in maintaining the health of the stock on which they prey. Shooting off hawks does not guarantee an increase of the population on which they subsist, for hawks can only take the weak, the sick, and the surplus beyond the carrying capacity of the habitat. Furthermore, certain animals, such as rats and ground squirrels, have a wide range of diet and a practically unlimited reproduction potential. Hawks and owls are a natural control on these animals, and elimination of the birds often results in an unchecked outbreak of pests (*See under Balance of Nature; Biological Control; and under Wildlife: The Wildlife Community*).

Today, the hawks and owls are protected in 19 states, and protection is given to some of them in another 18 states. As an awareness of the value of these birds develops, their protection will increase throughout the world.

—G.B.S.

Recommended Reading

Food Habits of Common Hawks — W. L. McAtee. United States Department of Agriculture, Circular 370, Washington, D.C.

Hawks Aloft: The Story of Hawk Mountain — Maurice Broun. Dodd Mead & Company, New York.

The Hawks of North America — John Richard May. National Association of Audubon Societies, New York.

Hawks, Owls, and Wildlife — Frank and John Craighead. The Staekpole Company, Harrisburg, Pennsylvania.

North American Birds of Prey — Alexander Sprunt, Jr. Harper & Brothers, New York.

Marsh Hawk

Other Common Names — Hen harrier, bullet hawk, harrier
Scientific Name — *Circus cyaneus*
Family — Accipitridae (hawks, Old World vultures, and harriers)
Order — Falconiformes
Size — Length, 19 to 22 inches
Range — Nests from northern and western Alaska, south to Baja California, and across southern Canada to Newfoundland, south to Virginia and west to Oklahoma, Kansas, Missouri, and the Middle West. South in winter to Florida, Bahamas, Gulf Coast, Cuba to southern Colombia. In Old World, from arctic tundra south to Mediterranean, Turkestan, Iran, and Southeast Asia

Closely related to the harriers of the Old World and the only representative of the harrier group in North America, the marsh hawk is a bird of open country, spending much of its time soaring above fields, marshes, and plains in search of food. Although the sexes differ in plumage, both male and female can be distinguished by a white patch on the rump. Female marsh hawks are brown above and light brown below with streaks running the length of the body. The tail is barred with black and buff. The adult male is a striking bird that resembles a gull because of its white underparts, black-tipped wings, and equal adeptness on the wing.

It has been claimed that the marsh hawk is responsible for heavy losses to poultry; however, it feeds on small birds and rodents when they are available. Studies made of the stomach contents of marsh hawks collected in Nevada showed that the birds' diet there consisted entirely of lizards. Again, in Georgia the

Adult male marsh hawk flying (left); female flying (right); immature, (perched)

cotton rat accounted for 84 percent of the marsh hawks' food. (Cotton rats often feed heavily on the eggs of the bobwhite quail, a much-sought gamebird.) Before the 1860's all of the rice produced in the United States was from plantations in North and South Carolina. The crop losses to bobolinks feeding on the rice was estimated to be in excess of two million dollars. The marsh hawk was a positive factor in keeping the loss from being even greater, because of its habit of flushing out bobolinks and feeding on them (*See under Balance of Nature, and Wildlife: The Wildlife Community*).

Marsh hawks nest on the ground in marshes or on prairies, mostly near water. Four to six pale, bluish-white eggs are laid in a nest built of sticks, grasses, and feathers, the nest sometimes develops into a large platform from continuous use over a period of several years. Both sexes help with the construction of the nest, the incubation, and the care of the young.   —A.S., Jr.

Food Habits of Hawks

Dead hawks strung on a wire fence are seen too often. It means that some people kill hawks without realizing that most of them are now protected by law in all but a few states. Why hawks are protected will be understood better after studying the diagram (*opposite page*). It is based on studies by the United States Department of Agriculture of 5,185 hawk stomachs (*See under Protection of Birds*).

'Living Mousetraps'

The hawks most commonly shot, such as the redtails on the fence, are the ones that soar in wide circles in the sky and perch conspicuously in the open. These are the hawks that feed mostly on insects and rodents—that's why they are often called "living mousetraps" (*See under Buteo*).

A Job for Every Hawk

The small creatures that hawks eat

WHAT HAWKS EAT

The numbers refer to percentages of various prey foods found in the stomachs of 5,185 hawks as based on studies made by the United States Dept. of Agriculture.

BROAD-WINGED HAWK Insects 39.7, Frogs, Snakes 30.9, Rats and Mice 23, Small Birds 3.4, Aquatic 2, Gamebirds .5, Rabbits .5

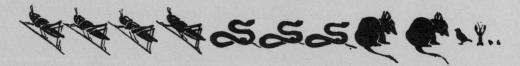

RED-SHOULDERED HAWK Insects 32, Rats and Mice 28, Frogs and Snakes 25, Aquatic 5.3, Small Birds 6.5, Poultry 1.4, Gamebirds .9, Rabbits .9

RED-TAILED HAWK Rats and Mice 53, Insects 10.5, Rabbits and Squirrels 9.3, Small Birds 9.2, Poultry 6.3, Frogs and Snakes 6.1, Gamebirds 2.1, Aquatic 1.5

ROUGH-LEGGED HAWK Rats and and Mice 72, Rabbits and Squirrels 8.6, Insects 6.5, Small Birds 4.3, Gamebirds 4.3, Aquatic 2.2, Frogs and Snakes 2.1

FERRUGINOUS ROUGHLEG Rodents 54, Rabbits and Squirrels 2.9, Insects 9, Gamebirds 4, Small Birds 4

SWAINSON'S HAWK Rodents 48, Insects 29.5, Snakes and Frogs 12, Small Birds 5.6, Rodents 3.7, Gamebirds .6, Aquatic .6

SPARROW HAWK Insects 63.5, Rats and Mice 20.3, Small Birds 8.4, Frogs and Snakes 7.8

COOPER'S HAWK Small Birds 55, Rats and Mice 17, Gamebirds 12, Poultry 10, Insects 5.3, Rabbits 1.7, Frogs, etc. 1

SHARP-SHINNED HAWK Small Birds 96.4, Rats and Mice 2.6, Insects .7, Frogs .1, Rabbits .1, Poultry .1

MARSH HAWK Small BIRDS 41, Rats and Mice 33, Rabbits and Squirrels 9, Gamebirds 7.2, Frogs etc. 4.1, Insects 2.3, Poultry 2.4, Aquatic .1

breed so rapidly that there is an important job for every hawk to do. If rats, mice, rabbits, squirrels, and gophers are not controlled by hawks, owls and other predators, they sometimes do extensive damage to agriculture. There can be no doubt that hawks have great value to the farmer and the land alike.

The Wildlife Community

The smaller long-tailed hawks that feed mostly on small birds are not seen very often because they do not soar in circles and usually perch under cover. The eating of small birds by hawks is nature's way of controlling their numbers so as to maintain a balanced and therefore healthy wildlife community (See also Wildlife: The Wildlife Community).

Know Your Hawks

Learn to identify the various hawks in your vicinity and observe their food habits. A Minnesota farmer reported to the National Audubon Society that, in one day, he watched a red-tailed hawk capture 32 mice that were turned up while he disked his field. He added that all hawks and owls are protected on his property, not just in view of their economic value but because he enjoys watching them.

HAWK MOTH

The members of this family that feed by day are often called hummingbird moths, because they are similar in size and in their habit of hovering over an open blossom. They are handsome moths, with stocky bodies and narrow, rapidly vibrating wings. They have long, coiled tongues and feed upon nectar.

The larvae of this family are distinguished by the thornlike projection—on the eighth abdominal segment—that gives them the name of hornworm. Some, such as the tomato and the tobacco hornworms, are crop pests.

—G.B.S.

HAWKWEED
Field Hawkweed
Other Common Names—King devil
Scientific Name—Hieracium pratense
Family—Compositae (composite family)
Range—Gaspe Peninsula, Quebec, to Ontario; south to Nova Scotia, New England, Long Island, North Carolina, and Tennessee
Habitat—Clearings, pastures, and grasslands
Time of Blooming—May through August

Orange Hawkweed
Other Common Names—Devil's paintbrush, Marguerite rouge, bouquets rouge
Scientific Name—Hieracium aurantiacum
Family—Compositae (composite family)
Range—Newfoundland to Minnesota, south to Novia Scotia, New England, Virginia, Ohio, northern Indiana, Illinois, and Iowa
Habitat—Clearings and fields
Time of Blooming—June through August

Hawkweeds cover the fields with blankets of yellow and orange during the summer. They are very hardy and tend to crowd out the farmers' crops. Like all members of the composite family, hawkweeds produce many tiny flowers in a compact group and every flower is capable of producing a seed. Each seed is equipped with hairs that act as a parachute to carry the seed on air currents, sometimes for very long distances. Every flower has a petal-like appendage, called a ray, which is notched at the top. Together they form the bright-colored heads that top the hairy stalks.

Both the orange and field hawkweeds are natives of Europe. The orange hawkweed flower stalk is seldom more than 1½ feet high but the field hawkweed's stem may reach a height of 3 feet.

Seeds of these weed plants furnish food for many of the winter resident birds, such as sparrows and their relatives, redpolls, goldfinches, and siskins. The blue and ruffed grouse eat the hairy, basal leaves of the hawkweed as

Field hawkweed and orange hawkweed

leaves have sharp teeth of two different sizes along each edge.

The hop hornbeam, or ironwood, has scaly brown bark, in contrast to the smooth gray of the hornbeam. The nut is enclosed in an envelope that is joined to a number of others in a structure that resembles the fruit of the European hopvine. The tree is eastern, but spreads as far west as the Dakotas.

The alders are also in the Betulaceae. They are moisture-loving shrubs, common along streams and rivers and bordering swamps and bogs. They have blunter leaves than the birches; their bark is darker,. but with the same lenticels, those openings in the bark for the exchange of gases between the tissues and the atmosphere. Some of the alders are found only in eastern North America; speckled alder, hazel alder, and seaside alder are in this group. No alders occur naturally in the American Great Plains, but a number of species, such as red alder, white alder, and Arizona alder, are found in western North America, while the Sitka alder is Alaskan.

—G.B.S.

well as its seeds. White-tailed deer and mountain sheep eat the plant.

HAZEL

The family to which the hazels belong —the Betulaceae, or birch family—is distinguished by the long, thick catkin of male flowers and the shorter, stubbier female catkins. Since the female flowers are pollinated by the wind, the male flowers produce great quantities of pollen. All of the trees in this family have leaves that are simple, alternate, and toothed.

The beaked hazel, or hazelnut, is a common shrub in eastern North America, ranging from Newfoundland to Georgia. Each nut has a pointed tip, where the scales that surround it meet in a projection. The California hazel, growing from Canada to central California, is a small tree. The American hornbeam, an eastern tree that grows as far west as Texas and Minnesota, has three lobed bracts (specialized leaves) around each nut. The

HEATHER
Purple Mountain Heather

Other Common Names—Brewer's mountain heather, alpine heather
Scientific Name—*Phyllodoce breweri*
Family—Ericaceae (heath family)
Range—Mount Shasta region, southward through the Sierra Nevada to the San Bernardino Mountains, California
Habitat—Rocky ledges on mountain heights
Time of Blooming—July to August

Purple mountain heather grows on very high mountains—up to 12,000 feet. It is a small shrub, from four inches to a foot high, and is found in both northern and southern mountains. The rosy flowers are saucer-shaped and have many long stamens. The leaves are evergreen and stand straight out from the stem. These little shrubs grow in wet, soggy ground and even in July the snow is not far away

Alpine heather

from them. Near them one finds cassiope, another alpine shrub. Its flowers are white and bell-shaped, like lily of the valley. The stems are all completely covered by the tiny leaves that lie flat over each other.

HEDGE

The line of bushes separating two open fields is termed a hedge, or hedge-row. It is a richer habitat for wildlife than the fields that it divides, for it offers shelter within close distance to the grains, grasses, or row crops among which the smaller field dwellers must feed. Some of our highest populations of nesting songbirds—up to 20 pairs or more per acre of land—nest in hedge-rows. Taller bushes in the hedgerow may be used as lookout towers by flycatchers, shrikes, and hawks that perch above the grassland while looking about for a possible meal. It is a combination of such factors that makes hedgerows so desirable for the propagation of wildlife. In certain parts of the world, England particularly where populations have settled most intensely, hedgerows have become one of the last refuges of wildlife. (*See also Edge Effect*)   —G.B.S.

Hedges of Multiflora Rose

Multiflora rose hedges are "room and board" for many kinds of wildlife. For years the United States Department of Agriculture has been publicizing this plant's multiple-use in fulfilling farm conservation practices. Yet, it was not until a complete winter-wildlife study of 300 yards of multiflora rose hedge—both quantitative and qualitative—was made, that it was realized in how many different ways it serves wildlife. The studies were made during the winter of 1958-1959 at the Aullwood Audubon Center of the National Audubon Society near Dayton, Ohio.

The hedge investigated was planted in the spring of 1953 as one year seedlings at a distance of 18 inches apart. By 1958 the thorny canes had extended upward to a height of five to seven feet before they began to droop, umbrellalike. The dense, thorny tangle of branches was already at the stage to discourage any large animal from passing through the hedge, and thus might serve as a fence for livestock.

In the winter of 1958-1959 the hedge was heavily laden with bright red berries that furnished many animals with food. Song- and gamebirds fed on the berries during the winter months—bobwhite, pheasant, robin, mockingbird, cedar waxwing, cardinal, tree sparrow, bluebird, song sparrow, goldfinch, junco, and chickadee. The berries were of particular importance in serving many birds with an emergency food supply when snow covered their natural food. The mockingbird, however, fed on the berries by preference, and one mockingbird established a feeding territory and successfully protected a small section of the hedge against other species of birds throughout most of the winter. In addition to the birds, various wild, four-footed animals fed regularly on the berries or green vegetation of the hedge—cottontail rabbits, white-footed mice, red foxes, and opossums.

The dense, entangled canes of the multiflora rose suited the nesting requirements of many animals. In the 300 yards of hedge, four different species of birds nested in the summer of 1958—the brown thrasher, cardinal, catbird, and field sparrow. Under the hedge the nesting conditions met the special needs of three species of mammals—the short-tailed shrew, meadow mouse, and woodchuck.

Multiflora rose attracts many kinds of insects. During the winter census 12 abandoned paper nests of wasps, 15 egg cases of praying mantises, and various kinds of moth cocoons—48 of bagworm, 8 of white-winged tussock moth, 3 of cecropia, and 1 of polyphemus—were discovered. All were attached to the thick canes.

This particular winter's study gives some indication as to the many ways that multiflora rose serves wildlife. By furnishing an important food supply during critical periods and providing ideal nesting sites for many species, multiflora rose fulfills two vital wildlife requirements. In addition to helping wildlife, the hedge is an important factor in preventing soil erosion by serving as a windbreak and anchoring the soil against downhill water flow.

At least 19 species of songbirds nested in the summer of 1952 in hedgerows studied by the Illinois Natural History Survey. Of the 19 species found and identified by their nests, slightly more than 70 percent were warblers, field or song sparrows, catbirds, brown thrashers, or robins.

The figures were based on numbers of nests found in fence row plantings investigated by Illinois Natural History Survey researchers in Champaign, Ver-milion, and Piatt counties and in the Crab Orchard Lake area of Williamson County. The above-average numbers of bird species and their nests were found in pure plantings of multiflora rose, also in a mixture of multiflora rose and Morrow's honeysuckle. However, mixed plantings containing red cedar proved to be almost twice as popular with the birds as either of the others.

—W.B.S.

Birds and Hedgerows

How much more valuable than some crops is a natural hedgerow across a field. Birds, both resident and migrant, will prove this by finding shelter in it, by nesting in it, and using it as the vantage point from which they set out on forays, not only to get their insect food from shrubs and trees, but into adjacent fields to feed on myriads of weed seeds and insects (*See also Edge Effects*). Growing together in some hedgerows are enough shrubs, trees, and vines to support an entire bird sanctuary. Among the most attractive of the native North American dogwoods—always giving the flowering dogwood pre-eminence, of course—is the pagoda, or alternate-leaved, dogwood, *Cornus alternifolia*. It is a small tree, often growing in the hedgerow (*See under Dogwood*). It has an interesting manner of growth, branching in distinct whorls, which has gained it its name of pagoda. Its leaves are alternate on the twigs instead of opposite as in other dogwoods. The flowers are profuse, borne in creamy, flat-topped clusters; the fruit, on red stems, is bright blue. The fruit sometimes persists on the tree from mid-June to mid-October, but it seldom lasts into winter, for it is a prime favorite of such birds as cardinals, vireos, and cedar waxwings. Another native shrub of the hedgerows, silky cornel, *Cornus am-*

momum, is a dogwood that has small creamy white flowers in clusters, similar to those of the pagoda dogwood. However, its fruit is not so brilliant in color, being usually cadet-blue or white. When autumn brings a band of migrating bluebirds they will strip the silky dogwood bushes of their fruit.

Another shrub of a dense twiggy growth, which makes it exceedingly valuable as a nesting site for birds, is the panicled dogwood, *Cornus racemosa*. Its creamy flowers are followed by white fruits that are carried until the end of October, thus providing food for migrant bird visitors. These shrubs and the flowering dogwood, which is seldom absent from any country place, small or large, in the eastern states, attract at least 93 kinds of birds. They include, besides those mentioned, such desirable species as flickers, downy woodpeckers, kingbirds, catbirds, thrushes, and the beloved white-throated and song sparrows.

With the dogwoods grow the viburnums, some of which carry their fruit through the winter and well into the spring. In a dry shady corner under a large tree, the maple-leaved viburnum, *Viburnum acerifolium*, holds its fruit very well. It has dark blue berries and in the fall the leaves turn very unusual shades of soft pinkish-lavender and purple. The nannyberry, *Viburnum lentago*, one of the more common hedgerow shrubs, has cadet-blue, long-persistent fruit with a soft bloom. Other viburnums are the blackhaw, *Viburnum prunifolium*, the arrowwood, *Viburnum dentatum*, and withe rod, *Viburnum cassinoides*, all bearing blue-black fruit with a bloom. One of the thirty or more birds known to feed on viburnum berries is the yellow-billed cuckoo, which eats quantities of hairy caterpillars. Most birds regard these caterpillars as distasteful but this cuckoo eats so many of them that the lining of its stomach is set with a thick row of spiny bristles.

The most attractive native North American shrub is the common elderberry, *Sambucus canadensis*. In late May and early June, all through the East and Middle West, its creamy white flower clusters make an unforgettable part of the wayside beauty. Later it is so loaded with fruit that the bush is actually top-heavy. Although it reaches its greatest luxuriance of growth in moist ground, the elderberry is adaptable and can be grown in a naturalistic shrubbery border as well as in the hedgerow. With the growing appreciation of native species it will be more frequently seen than the once widely planted golden elder, a variety of the European elderberry.

The elderberry ranks next to raspberries and blackberries in its lure for the birds. It is known that over a hundred species eat its small black fruit and that of its close relative the red elder,

More than a hundred species of birds feed on the fruits of the elderberry

Hedgerows between fields offer cover to a variety of wildlife

Some 30 species of birds feed on the fruit of the blackhaw

Other Native Fruiting Trees and Shrubs of Hedgerows

Name	Fruit known to be eaten by
Bayberry........ *Myrica Pensylvanica* Fruit gray	85 kinds of birds including myrtle warbler, Carolina wren, tree swallow, downy woodpecker, bobwhite, thrasher, bluebird, and many others.
Bearberry....... *Arctostaphylos uva-ursi* Fruit red	34 kinds of birds including ruffed grouse, quail, and fox sparrow.
Blueberry....... *Vaccinium* spp. Fruit blue	93 kinds of birds including black-capped chickadee, kingbird, robin, hermit thrush, titmouse, cedar waxwing, thrasher, towhee, etc.
Wild cherries.. *Prunus* spp. Fruit red	84 kinds of birds including bluebird, flicker, woodpecker, catbird, bobwhite, cedar waxwing, goldfinch, and kingbird.
Chokeberry .... *Pyrus arbutifolia, Pyrus melanocarpa* Fruit red and black	21 kinds of birds including meadowlark and brown thrasher.
Crabapple...... *Pyrus* spp. Fruit yellow and red	43 kinds of birds including pine grosbeak, cedar waxwing, robin, ruffed grouse, ring-necked pheasant, purple finch, etc.
Hawthorn...... *Crataegus* spp., from 10 to 20 ft. Fruit red	39 kinds of birds including ruffed grouse, pine grosbeak, purple finch, and robin.
Holly, American, *Ilex opaca* and other spp. Fruit red	48 kinds of birds including bobwhite, hermit thrush, bluebird, cedar waxwing, catbird, flicker, thrasher, etc.
Huckleberry ... *Gaylussacia* spp. Fruit black	46 kinds of birds including robin, towhee, and pine grosbeak.
Mountain ...... ash, *Sorbus americana* to 30 ft. Fruit red	13 kinds of birds including Bohemian and cedar waxwings, Baltimore oriole, robin, catbird, evening and pine grosbeaks.
Pokeberry ...... *Phytolacca americana* Perennial, dies to ground each fall Fruit purple	52 kinds of birds including flicker, kingbird, bluebird, catbird, robin, cardinal, etc.
Rose, wild ..... *Rosa* spp. Fruit red	38 kinds of birds including ruffed grouse and bobwhite.
Spicebush...... *Lindera Benzoin* Fruit red	17 kinds of birds including wood thrush, veery, kingbird, and red-eyed vireo.

(*See also Plants and Water for Birds*)

Sambucus pubens. Flocking to these two shrubs come flickers, woodpeckers, bluebirds, thrushes, and the kingbird.

At frequent intervals in the hedgerows one finds native North American red cedar, *Juniperus virginiana.* This close-growing evergreen provides birds with an all-year-round haven. It is the hostelry of more than fifty species, including such valuable garden allies as flickers, bluebirds, robins, waxwings, purple finches, mockingbirds, and the myrtle warbler. In it these birds find not only shelter but food in every month especially in spring when fruit is scarce (*See under Cedar and under Juniper*).

Often in the natural hedgerow is found a mulberry tree, either the native North American red mulberry, *Morus rubra*, or the naturalized Asiatic white mulberry, *Morus alba*. Birds flock to these trees from far and wide, and no better protection for cherries, strawberries, and other early fruits can be provided than a few mulberries, for the birds always prefer wild fruit to the cultivated varieties. Both pistillate and staminate forms should be planted, unless it is known that there are other trees in the neighborhood. More than fifty kinds of birds are known to eat the fruits of mulberry; among them are robins, bluebirds, catbirds, brown thrashers, various woodpeckers, orioles, kingbirds, cuckoos, scarlet tanagers, and the cardinal (*See Mulberry*).   —M.M.

HEDGE BINDWEED
Other Common Names—Wild morning glory
Scientific Names—*Convolvulus sepium*
Family—Convolvulaceae (convolvulus family)
Range—Newfoundland to British Columbia; south to Florida, Alabama, Missouri, New Mexico, and Oregon
Habitat—Thickets, shores, and stone walls
Time of Blooming—Mid-May to September

This morning-glory vine is one of the most common members of the Convolvulvus family. Its bell-shaped white or pink flowers are about two inches long. The stems of this vine are from 3 to 10 feet long. They trail over the ground or twine about other plants, trying to get into the light where their leaves can manufacture food. Because of this habit they often become troublesome weeds.

The flowers grow along the stem at the axils of the arrow-shaped leaves. They are visited by hummingbird moths and hummingbirds, whose long tongues are well adapted to getting to the base

Hedge bindweed

of the deep funnel-like blossoms. They are also visited by various species of bees, which are guided by the white streaks, or pathfinders, as they crawl into the flower and probe through one of the five narrow passages to reach the nectar.

There are about 200 species of morning glories and most of these grow in tropical regions. The sweet potato, originally from Central America, is a member of this family. A number of the wild morning glories have been transferred to our gardens where they thrive unchanged. They are rapid growers and are commonly used about homes to cover walls and fences during the summer months. Hedge bindweed is on the conservation list of some states.

HELLBENDER (*See under Amphibian*)

HELL-DIVER (*See under Grebe*)

HEMLOCK

Hemlocks are distinguished by their small flattened needles that have two white stripes on the under surface. These stripes are more or less distinct, depending on the species. The needles are attached to woody stalks arranged in two rows along the sides of the twigs and do not attach directly to the twig as do the leaves of many other species of the pine family. On the top of the twig, and extending in the same direction as it, is a third row of inconspicuous needles.

Four species of hemlock occur in North America. In the eastern United States and Canada, the eastern hemlock, *Tsuga canadensis,* is a common tree of northern slopes in forest areas. From uplands of West Virginia to Georgia, a second, smaller hemlock, the Carolina hemlock, *Tsuga caroliniana,* grows. In western North America, two similar species, the western hemlock, *Tsuga heterophylla,* and the mountain hemlock, *Tsuga mertensiana,* share a nearly identical range.
—G.A.B.

Eastern Hemlock

Other Common Names—Canadian hemlock, spruce-pine
Scientific Name—*Tsuga canadensis*
Family—Pinaceae (pine family)
Range—Nova Scotia, southern Quebec, and southern Ontario; Maine to northeastern Minnesota; south to Long Island, northern New Jersey, and eastern Ohio, and in Appalachians to northern Alabama and northern Georgia
Habitat—A graceful forest tree of cool, shady woodlands around lakes, streams, ponds
Leaves—Flat, dark yellowish-green needles about one-half inch long, growing in two irregular ranks along the sides of the twig and striped below with two whitish bands, giving the foliage a silvery look when twisted. New spring growth is a bright emerald green
Bark—Smooth and gray when young, later peeling into darker squarish flakes; when thicker, deeply cracked and of a reddish-brown tone. When cut, the bark shows streaks of rust and purplish-pink
Flowers—The one-fourth inch, conelike female blossoms are pink and green and are borne at the tips of the branches; the much smaller inconspicuous male blossoms are yellow and farther back on the twig. Usually blooms in May
Fruit—Small, compact, smooth oval cones, one-half to three-fourth inches long, hanging from outer twigs; shedding their small seeds in winter, and often remaining attached, though empty

Of all North American trees that flourish in cool, rather damp, shaded locations, the eastern hemlock is outstanding. Growing characteristically on the north side of slopes, ravines, and lake margins in New England and Appalachian forests, it has probably suffered as much from wasteful use as any other species. Hemlock bark has or has had a priority (over its wood) for the purpose of tanning leather, and not many years ago accounts of forest areas littered with stripped, unused trunks of this tree were common. The lumber, which has few outstanding properties, holds nails well and is used for general construction work and for pulp in making paper. At one time hemlocks 150 feet high and 5 or 6 feet through the trunk were cut, but now few trees are much over half these dimensions, for once past early "treehood" they grow quite slowly. In most areas this hemlock does not constitute a large part of the total forest; it usually occurs singly or in small groves among the deciduous trees, the tops of the larger specimens often standing well above the surrounding growth.

When very young, hemlocks growing on suitable locations have a fairly dense, good-looking foliage of glossy texture. The mature eastern hemlock tree is apt to have a rather irregular branching and foliage, which looks a bit thin and of dull color. The very tops of the trees blow to leeward, away from the prevailing wind.
—M.B.

The eastern hemlock grows in cool, shaded forests. Its needles are flattened, and its cones often remain on the tree after opening. The bark of older trees is reddish-brown and forms square, flaky blocks

Mountain Hemlock
Other Common Names — Black hemlock
Scientific Name — *Tsuga mertensiana*
Family — Pinaceae (pine family)
Range — From southern Alaska, south along the coast to Oregon; and from southeastern British Columbia and western Montana, south in the interior to central California on the high slopes of the Sierra Nevada
Habitat — In North America, mostly alpine. In good stands it averages 75 to 100 feet with trunk diameters up to 3 or 4 feet. Rugged and stalwart, with thick, sprucelike foliage, it has stiff, downswept branches and often grows in precipitous and rocky sites. It occurs from sea level to 10,000 feet but is stunted or even prostrate at timberline
Leaves — Plump, blue-green needles with constricted, stemlike bases, up to one inch long and growing from all sides of the twig
Bark — Dark cinnamon brown, sometimes purplish, with vertical grooves and some horizontal cracking
Flowers — Male: violet-purple on hairy, drooping stems. Female: erect and purplish to yellow-green
Fruit — Elongate cones usually one to three inches long, hanging in clusters near the ends of the branches. Rich purple or yellow-green before ripening, brown in autumn

The name mountain hemlock is sometimes used for a rather small species, *Tsuga caroliniana*, that occurs in or near the high rainfall belt of the southern Appalachian Mountains, but more often it refers to this western tree. It frequently grows in picturesque form in craggy mountainous situations that are its home. It is a tree of robust trunk with a relatively small volume of foliage and the stumps of a few dead branches jutting out here and there — the type of tree that almost always appears to be part of a movie location for a film about wild, unexplored territory in the West. And so it often is. Fortunately this interesting species is not in high demand for lumber, being of moderate size compared to the giants of the western forests (*See Douglas-fir, Cedar, and Redwood*), and apt to grow in inaccessible places.

Western Hemlock
Other Common Names — Hemlock-spruce, hemlock, Alaska-pine
Scientific Name — *Tsuga heterophylla*
Family — Pinaceae (pine family)
Range — Same as the mountain hemlock's but more limited in the Sierra Nevada
Habitat — Cool, moist, usually northern mountain slopes
Leaves — Similar to mountain hemlock's
Bark — Similar to mountain hemlock's
Flower — Similar to mountain hemlock's
Fruit — Small cones, seven-eighths of an inch long with wavy scale margins

The Washington state tree rather generally referred to as western hemlock is a much larger species, more abundant, and a prominent lumber tree. With trunk diameters up to ten feet (a figure well above average) and with a good straight grain, its rather light wood is better for most purposes than others of this group. Various medium-stress construction jobs are done with western hemlock; boxes, barrels, sheathing, and wood pulp comprise other common uses. Because it reproduces rapidly and is tolerant of shade, it does well even when a bit crowded. The larger dangers to these trees are probably too frequent harvesting, fire, and windfall. — M.H.B.

HEPATICA
Other Common Names — Liverleaf
Scientific Name — *Hepatica americana*
Family — Ranunculaceae (crowfoot family)
Range — Nova Scotia to Manitoba, south to northern Florida, Alabama, and Missouri
Habitat — Dry woods
Time of Blooming — January to early June

Hepaticas often bloom so early in the

Liverleaf hepatica

spring that they push their way up through the snow. The stems of the flowers and new leaves are heavily coated with hairlike projections that expand and contract as freezing and thawing takes place. This modification protects the plant from the loss of too much moisture.

The hepatica's leaves are semievergreen, three-parted, frequently reddish underneath, and about two inches long. Strange to say, the flowers have no petals. The colored parts that look like petals are the sepals. Close beneath the colored sepals are three tiny leaves that many mistake for sepals. The plant grows from three to six inches high.

There are only two species of hepaticas in North America and they both occur in the eastern states as well as in Alaska and Europe. The flowers vary in color from white to pink or blue and are sometimes fragrant. *Hepatica americana* is on the conservation lists of many states.

Long ago, because people thought the leaf of this plant was shaped like a liver, it was frequently crushed and taken as an antidote for liver trouble.

HERBICIDE

An herbicide is a chemical designed to kill plants. When intelligently used, it is a tool for controlling vegetation relatively cheaply. Some herbicides are selective, killing only broad-leaved plants, or only narrow-leaved (grasses, cattails, etc.) plants.

Like all other chemical pesticides, the herbicides need to be used selectively, that is, for the control of only those individual plant species that are causing problems. The use of blanket sprays along roadsides or other rights-of-ways, in agriculture or forestry, or in spraying lawns for crabgrass, are wasteful and objectionable ways of applying herbicides because the effect on habitats is often too drastic and because drift of the chemical spray is almost certain to damage adjacent areas where no plant kill is desired. Private landowners thus affected may sue for damages in such cases, and the spray operators will be held liable by the courts.

Herbicides will become truly useful management tools when (1) the trouble is taken to identify the handful of plant species that cause problems; (2) when it is recognized that each of these species has different growth habits; and, (3) when a willingness is developed to use herbicides selectively instead of spraying them indiscriminately. In so doing, the practice of calling all low woody vegetation "brush" and all herbaceous growth "weeds"—something to be eliminated—will be stopped. Loose terms, such as these, mean nothing except that the user is prejudiced about something he doesn't really understand.

In general, when selectively used, such long-used herbicides as 2,4-D and 2,4,5-T Dalapon appear to be harmless to animals. Certain other herbicides have proven dangerous and all of them must be used expertly. Just as drugs are used only with a doctor's prescription, these chemicals should be employed only with the guidance of a competent biologist.

—R.C.C.

HERON

Occasionally the newspapers carry the picture of a long-necked, long-legged bird that has come to grief in the city. Few recognize it for what it is. Some people call it a crane, others a stork, and others think it must be some strange bird that has escaped from a zoo. In the Northeast, almost any bird answering the above description is likely to be a member of the heron family. Egret is the common name for the two white members of the family; members of another group in the same family are known as bitterns (*See under Bittern and under Egret*).

Actually, despite the general ignorance concerning them, herons are not rare. They are numerous along the shores of rivers, lakes, saltwater marshes, and bays. They are true wading birds and many can be found in remote marshes. Today, in these marshes, a persistent observer can still see every species of heron found in them by the first settlers over 300 years ago—nine species in all. This speaks well for the herons' alertness and wariness, as they are large and usually fairly conspicuous in the flat open areas they frequent.

One of the largest herons native to the United States is the great blue heron, *Ardea herodias*. It is a stately bird, standing over four feet high, with a wingspread that may exceed six feet. It occurs all over North America. In the northern part of the range it is a migrant, going south in winter. Great blue herons nest in large colonies, building crude platform nests of sticks and twigs high in the trees of swamps, remote from the danger of much molestation by man. Occasionally the nests are built in low shrubs or on the ground.

After the breeding season is over they wander, and from mid-July until the marshes freeze they are a common sight in any extensive marsh. They frequently travel hundreds of miles from the nesting colony, and are as likely to go north as south. Thus herons seen in the late summer are not necessarily on their way south from northern breeding colonies.

From July to September this wandering brings three southern herons to northeastern marshes. They are easy to spot because they are white. The largest, the common egret, *Casmerodius albus*, is about the size of a great blue heron. It can be identified readily by its bright yellow bill. During the breeding season it wears beautiful long feathers on its back, the famous aigrettes of the millinery trade. Much smaller than the American egret is the snowy egret, *Leucophoyx thula*, another pure white species and among the most beautiful of the American marshbirds. It can be identified by a very thin black bill; but the most notable characteristic is the color of its feet, which are bright yellow in sharp contrast to black legs. It also wears aigrettes on its back during the breeding season. The third of the southern herons to be found in the late summer is often difficult to identify. It is the little blue heron, *Florida caerulea*, in its first-year plumage. The young birds are white.

The most common heron, the green heron, *Butorides virescens*, is so small and inconspicuous that it is frequently overlooked. It is to be found near every body of water, salt or fresh, large or small. The only heron likely to be found along small brooks, it is dark, rather short-necked for a heron, and looks like a crow when it flies. Bright orange-yellow legs are its best field mark.

All herons can apparently feed during either day or night. However, the majority seem to prefer to eat in the daytime. Being quite gregarious, they usually gather in their roosts at sunset. Two species prefer to feed at night and are called night herons. The black-crowned night herons, *Nycticorax nycticorax*, are commonly known as the quawks from their call. They are best seen when flying out to their feeding grounds at sunset. The young birds are a dull brown, spotted and streaked with white, while the adults are a beautiful

*Great blue **herons***

soft gray and white, with black on their backs and the tops of their heads. Sometimes an observer also sees the southern yellow-crowned night heron, *Nyctanassa violacea*.

These beautiful marshbirds have suffered much persecution by man. Their gorgeous plumage made them favorites among milliners a generation ago. As a result, high prices were offered for heron feathers; finally, as the birds became scarce, aigrettes from the backs of white herons were bringing their weight in gold. Herons, in common with many other birds, put on their finest plumage for the breeding season. To get the plumes before they became too worn, the hunters raided the nesting colonies, or rookeries. In order to get all the birds in the colony, the hunters waited until the herons had young in the nests so that the shooting of some would not cause the rest to leave. Then they shot both parents, often right on the nest, and left the young to starve.

Many states passed laws protecting herons, but such laws did little good as long as there was a market for the plumage. The National Audubon Society paid wardens to guard some of the egret colonies, but much illegal killing still went on. One of the early Audubon wardens, Guy Bradley, was actually murdered by plume hunters, and the community was so unsympathetic to any effort to protect birds that his murderers were acquitted (*See under National Audubon Society*).

Finally, in 1910, after a fight lasting five years, conservationists succeeded in getting a first bill through the New York legislature that helped stop the demand for heron feathers. This law did more to save the herons than had dozens of local laws against killing them. Once the New York market declined, the killing stopped and the herons began to increase. The vigorous efforts of the Audubon Society saved them from extinction now, after years of protection, they are again becoming common. Herons

have full federal as well as state protection and it is at all times illegal to kill them.

Unfortunately, an even less defensible killing of herons still goes on. In the case of the plume hunter, some use was made of the feathers and the hunter himself did it to earn a living. Today's heron shooting is just plain wanton killing. Being large and conspicuous, herons, along with hawks, are frequent targets for gunners. Occasionally they try to justify their actions by charging that herons are destructive to fishes. Herons do eat fishes, but not in critical quantities. Hundreds of stomachs of every species of heron have been examined by the United States Fish and Wildlife Service to learn exactly what they feed upon. These studies reveal that they depend upon frogs, salamanders, crayfishes, eels, sankes, and insects, as well as upon fishes (*See under Fish-eating Bird*).

Herons attracted to fish hatcheries by the large concentrations of fishes are sometimes killed by hatchery employees. Should fish hatcheries continue to increase as they have in recent years, and this practice be permitted, it would be just a question of time before the herons were exterminated. Fortunately hatcheries can be screened at small cost to prevent wild birds and mammals from getting at the fishes and every year more hatcheries are being properly screened. It is by such steps that the heron population will and must be saved. —R.H.P.

Recommended Reading

Bird leaflets on herons, Nos. 54, 66, 98, 109, 130, and 141. National Audubon Society.
Birds Around New York—A. D. Cruickshank. American Museum of Natural History, New York.
Birds in Relation to Fishes—C. Cottam. Leaflet B.S. 83, United States Department of Agriculture, Washington, D.C.
The Book of Birds—T. G. Pearson. National Geographic Society, Washington, D.C.
Distribution and Migration of North American Herons—W. W. Cooke. Bulletin No. 45, Biological Survey, United States Department of Agriculture, 1913.

Great Blue Heron
Other Common Names—Blue crane
Scientific Name—*Ardea herodias*
Family—Ardeidae (herons and bitterns)
Order—Ciconiiformes
Size—Length, 46 inches
Range—Breeds from southern Alaska, central Saskatchewan, northern Ontario, central Quebec, and Nova Scotia south to the West Indies and Mexico. Winters all along the Pacific Coast and on the Atlantic Coast as far north as New York and occasionally New England; also southern United States south to Colombia and Venezuela

Although there are large sections of the United States and Canada where there are no known colonies of great blue herons, they have a wide breeding range and nest in a surprising variety of places—in the tops of tall cypress trees in southern swamps; in red maples, ashes, elms, or tamaracks in the North; among cacti, yuccas, and on the ground on some of the coastal islands of Texas; and even on rocky ledges in a few arid sections of the West.

Few people are fortunate enough to have seen a great blue heron colony, but nearly everyone has either seen the bird somewhere or lives in a locality where it can be seen, for there is scarcely a region where it does not occur at some time or other. It travels high in its wanderings, its telescopic sight enabling it to see small bits of water at a great distance. The bird is almost universally called a crane, but the real crane, which is not found so widely, flies with its neck stretched out. Like all herons, the great blue flies with its head drawn back to the shoulders. Except for the great white heron of southern Florida, this species is the largest of its family, with a wingspread of about six feet.

The nest is usually a large platform of sticks. Four or five light greenish-blue eggs are laid. Incubation takes about four weeks. The young are fed by regurgitation; that is, the food is first partially digested in the parent's crop

Great blue heron

and then given to the young. The tussle, when the eager young bird grabs hold of its parent's bill, looks like some sort of wrestling match. The older offspring are fed on whole fishes, as much as 8 or 10 inches long.

The great blue heron usually fishes along the water's edge. Sometimes it stealthily stalks through the shallows, its long legs keeping its feathers above the water. At other times it stands perfectly still like a statue. Although the bill is pointed straight ahead, the eyes of the bird are so placed that they can focus downward on any unwary fish that swims around its feet. When the time comes to act, the long neck suddenly darts forward, and the prey is either stabbed through by the open bill or seized crosswise. Deftly the fish is turned around and swallowed headfirst—whole.

Although great blue herons can eat fishes that are as much as a foot long, they sometimes attempt to swallow even larger fishes. More than once, a great blue heron has been found strangled to death by a fish too large to swallow.

From those parts of the United States and Canada where water freezes during the winter months, the great blue heron migrates. There is a large flight out of the northern sections between September and November. Some hardy birds attempt to spend the winter as far north as New England, southern Ontario, and southern Minnesota, but when cold snaps freeze up their fishing spots they have a hard time; unless they can find mice to feed on, they are often found in a starved condition. On the warmer Pacific slopes they are not faced with such hardships. —A.B., Jr.

Little Blue Heron
Other Common Names—Blue egret
Scientific Name—*Florida caerulea*
Family—Ardeidae (herons and bitterns)
Order—Ciconiiformes
Size—Length, 24 inches
Range—Breeds from Delaware, North Carolina, southern Alabama, Arkansas, and eastern Texas south to Central America. Winters from South Carolina southward. Wanders occasionally to midwestern United States, southern Canada, and New England

This species is perhaps one of the most abundant of the herons found within the limits of the United States. Its favorite haunts are freshwater swamps and marshes, where it procures its food of minnows, frogs, water insects, and other small animals. It is especially at home about the small ponds and lakes that are to be found scattered throughout the flatwoods and pine barrens of the South. It is one of the characteristic birds of such regions and often may be seen standing motionless in the shallow water or, if surprised, flapping its way to some other feeding ground.

The little blue heron is often confused with the snowy egret since it passes through a white phase in which all stages of intergradation are exhibited, from almost pure white to spots and splotches of blue, before the typical adult plumage is attained. White individuals have been found breeding. The feet and legs of immature birds are yellowish-green. This should serve to distinguish it from the snowy egret, which has black legs and yellowish feet.

Little blue herons nest in colonies of varying size, often in company with other herons. The nest is a rude platform of sticks in bushes or small trees. From three to four pale blue eggs are laid.

Little blue heron, adult (below); immature (above)

Green heron

Green Heron
Other Common Names — Green bittern, shitepoke
Scientific Name — *Butorides virescens*
Family — Ardeidae (herons and bitterns)
Order — Ciconiiformes
Size — Length, 18 inches
Range — Southern Ontario and Alberta, western Washington, southern Nevada, central Arizona, north-central Texas, central Michigan and Minnesota, Maine, and southern New Brunswick south through Mexico, West Indies, and Central America to northern South America

This little bird is seldom seen until it springs into the air with a loud high-pitched *skeow* and flies away low over the water. Usually solitary, it is encountered on the banks of even the smallest tree-bordered streams and ponds.

The green heron's long neck can be extended with lightninglike rapidity when prey is sighted, but normally its neck is so drawn in that the bird does not look much like a heron. Its entire appearance changes, however, when alarmed and nervous, and it is hardly recognizable as the same bird. It walks about nervously, twitching its tail downward, with its head held high on fully extended neck and alternately erecting and lowering the feathers of its crest.

Necessity rather than instinct often makes it a solitary nester in some shrub or low tree near its chosen pond or stream. Where the more ample food supply offered by an extensive marsh permits a greater concentration, one occasionally finds these herons nesting in typical heron style in colonies of 20 or 30 nests. They build a flimsy platform of sticks. It is a wonder it holds the four or five greenish eggs, as they often can be seen from the ground right through the bottom of the nest.

The green heron's normal food is about one-half fish with the balance of unequal quantities of crayfishes and aquatic insects.

Black-crowned Night Heron
Other Common Names — Gardenian heron, quawk
Scientific Name — *Nycticorax nycticorax*
Family — Ardeidae (herons and bitterns)
Order — Ciconiiformes
Size — Length, 25 inches
Range — Worldwide. Southern Canada, Washington, Idaho, and Nova Scotia south to Tierra del Fuego. In Old World, Holland and South Africa. Also in Japan and India. Replaced by a related species in the Australian region

Birds that possess an adaptability that has permitted them to achieve worldwide distribution are better able than most to withstand the changes wrought by civilization. The black-crowned night heron is an outstanding example, since it is still common near many of our largest cities. It is nocturnal, and during daylight hours the birds gather in roosts in isolated groves of trees, preferably

Black-crowned night heron, young and adult (below); yellow-crowned night heron, young and adult (above)

dense evergreens, where they are seldom noticed. Its nesting colonies are usually in dense second-growth woodland, where the nests are 15 to 30 feet from the ground. The number of nests varies from a few dozen to thousands. Herons are quite gregarious and several other species often nest with the black-crowned night heron.

The black-crown's food is about half fishes; the balance is crayfishes, aquatic insects, and frogs. Once thought to be detrimental to sport fishing, herons are now recognized as helpful, as they perform a very necessary weeding of fish populations. Fishes are so prolific that the available food supply is seldom sufficient to raise to maturity more than a small fraction of the young that hatch. Growth stagnation occurs unless natural enemies such as herons are present to thin the population as the fishes grow and need more food. If enough fishes are not removed to prevent this, few, if any, will reach maturity and legal fishing size.

Great White Heron
Other Common Names—Florida heron
Scientific Name—*Ardea occidentalis*
Family—Ardeidae (herons and bitterns)
Order—Ciconiiformes
Size—Length, 49 inches
Range—Southern Florida, West Indies (Cuba, Isle of Pines), coastal Yucatan, and Quintana Roo

This large snow-white bird is the largest American heron, yet it occupies the most restricted range of any of its group —indeed, of almost any bird in the United States.

The great white heron is quite conspicuous. Looming large against the green of mangrove-studded keys, or standing like marble-white statues amid the amazing colors of a shallow bay, they are visible for long distances. The greenish-yellow legs, lack of the streaming aigrette plumes, and more deliberate flight, as well as the larger size, dis-

Great white heron

tinguish it from the common, or American, egret, which is uncommon in the greater portion of the great white heron's range. However, in the Cape Sable region of Florida, the lower Everglades, and parts of the Ten Thousand Islands, where the common egret also occurs, close observation is needed to differentiate between the two.

Unlike others of its tribe, the great white heron does not congregate in large rookeries to nest. Two to four pairs will occupy one site, a few miles away half a dozen pairs will be on another, and ten miles further perhaps eight pairs will find a home. The largest concentrations hardly, if ever, reach 50 pairs, at least not in recent years.

The great white heron constructs its nest of large sticks, which are shaped into large bulky platforms. The hollow center is lined with grasses and other fine materials. The nests are built in low trees, usually on small mangrove-covered islands. Three pale blue-green eggs are laid.

HERRING

There are a great many different kinds of herrings. As a group they are the most important of man's food fishes. There are both marine and freshwater species. All are characterized by an elongated body. The skipjack herring is an interesting species found in both marine and fresh waters of the United States.

Skipjack
Other Common Names — Blue herring, river herring, golden shad
Scientific Name — *Alosa chrysochloris*
Family — Clupeidae (herrings)
Order — Clupeiformes
Size — Length, 16 to 20 inches
Range — North to the Great Lakes, south to southern Florida, east into the Atlantic, and west to about the eastern border of Texas

The skipjack is very streamlined. Weighing 1¼ to 3½ pounds, its body is slender and elliptical, with a sharply keeled belly. Its head is pointed and its lower jaw projects well ahead of its upper jaw. Its one dorsal fin is well developed, and its tail fin is deeply forked.

The skipjack's back is deep bluish-silver; its sides are more silvery. Its belly is silver-white or milk-white. Lines of one to nine dusky spots extend from over the rear of the gills, along the fish's upper sides.

The skipjack eats mostly other fishes. It often jumps clear of the water as it pursues its prey. Because it is particularly bony, the skipjack is not considered a good food fish.

Two of the many other important herrings are the Atlantic herring, *Clupea harengus harengus,* and the Pacific herring, *Clupea harengus pallasi.*   — M.R.

HERRING GULL (*See under Gull*)

HIBERNATION
Winter Sleep — Animals That Hibernate
Through the late summer and early fall many mammals appear to be more active. They are busily engaged in carrying a food supply to underground chambers in stumps or holes of trees in anticipation of the lean months ahead. Deer mice cram their cheek pouches with seeds, the red and gray squirrels are busily caching acorns and hickory nuts beneath the leaves, while the pika of the Rockies, a small relative of the rabbits and hares, is curing its winter hay pile on the steep mountainous slopes. All of these are active throughout the coldest weather of the year; winter holds no terror for such provident animals.

But what of those that practice no storage, and must flee the hostile zero weather if food is not available? Some species of bats migrate southward. Others, along with the ground squirrels, woodchucks, jumping mice, and many more, pass away the long winter months in an inactive state in which the body processes are greatly retarded, a condition known as hibernation.

Hibernation is common to many groups of animals. Numerous insects, snails, amphibians, and reptiles, as well as some mammals, meet the rigors of the winter season by becoming torpid and thus insensible to the cold. When the first skim ice forms on the margins of ponds, the frogs bury themselves in the mud and leaves of the bottom. Early frosts warn the toad that winter is not far off and with its horny heels it digs into the ground, burying itself below the frost line. Rattlesnakes, copperheads, and blacksnakes seek the shelter of a mountainous cave; red-bellied snakes may occupy an ant hill. Garter snakes may actually pass the winter in a spring, where the water never approaches the freezing point. Some butterflies winter in hollow logs, buildings, or other structures, taking again to the air with the first warm days of spring. The caterpillar of the beautiful viceroy butterfly, soon after emerging from the egg, constructs a *hibernaculum,* a shelter in which to pass the winter. On every hand, there is evidence of torpidity through the long months of snow and frost. A walk in the snow-carpeted woods reveals few signs of animal life: a few chickadees and nuthatches, and the tracks of a squirrel or a rabbit or two.

Some Theories of Hibernation

The phenomenon of hibernation has been studied by a great many scientists and the theories advanced to account for it are by no means in agreement.

With freezing temperatures and the consequent destruction of many food plants and small animal life, one might immediately consider the lack of suitable food to play an obvious role in hibernation. It is easy to understand why many insectivorous bats seek a cave in the late fall, to while away the winter months in close-packed balls of fur. All summer they have fattened on the abundant insect life, and with this source of food gone, they must either journey to a warmer climate or hibernate.

On the other hand, lack of food is not the only stimulus that may induce mammal hibernation. Consider the plump woodchuck of the clover field. During September every farm supports several of these big rodents. But the fall rains of Indian summer bring new verdure to the fields. Food is never more abundant for a vegetarian than in early October, but not a woodchuck is to be seen. All have retreated to their underground chambers, and already the deep sleep that is to last four months or more has begun.

The jumping mice have habits similar to the handsome deer mouse, at least in the summer. There is no reason to suspect their winter food should be different. Yet they, unlike the deer mice, go down into the soil with the first hard frosts, coiled into tight little fur balls of nearly frozen flesh.

Some have considered that the body temperature of a mammal must drop very low to induce hibernation. The skunk according to this theory is not a hibernator, for its body temperature does not drop markedly. Yet every observant trapper has noted that after the freezing weather of late November and early December, traps yield only the males. The female skunk and the young born during the previous spring are safely ensconced in their underground nests, and will not venture forth for many weeks.

Various factors responsible for this deathlike sleep may be long looked for, but one observation is evident. In order to hibernate, an animal must be fat. The woodchuck has doubled its weight from May to September, ground squirrels and jumping mice have a thick white layer of fat just under the skin. The more torpid an animal becomes, the thicker the layer of fat which guards its body. Those that fail to gather this protective coat often remain active well into the winter, and frequently succumb before they can prepare for the long winter sleep. When the fat is carefully scraped from a bat just entering the period of hibernation, it is found to constitute a third of the total weight of the animal.

Characteristics of Hibernation

As a ground squirrel or jumping mouse commences its long winter torpor, profound changes occur in its physiological behavior. Temperatures drop to that of the surroundings, or may even become lower. If the internal body temperature of the animal drops to the freezing point, its winter sleep ends in death. But hibernators are peculiarly adapted to resist freezing, for they almost always awaken when there is a sudden drop in the atmospheric temperature to freezing or lower. The temperature of most mammals approximates that of man, but during the profound sleep of hibernation, temperatures drop to a few degrees above the freezing point. The racoon, skunk, and bear, often considered to be hibernators, do not experience such low temperatures, although the thick insulating layer of fat which permits snow to cake and persist on the fur of a sleeping bear might lead one to believe otherwise. The winter temperature of bats usually approximates that of their cave surroundings, which usually remains relatively constant (50° to 60° F.) throughout the year in extensive caverns (*See Cave Life*).

During hibernation, respiration is greatly retarded. An active ground squirrel may, during the summer months, average 187 inspirations a minute, but in the deathlike torpor of January, the inspirations are reduced to 1 to 4 a minute. Inspiration in torpid woodchucks can barely be detected, and may occur only at intervals of 4 to 6 minutes. One hibernating jumping mouse under close observation gave no indication of respiration for 15 minutes.

A much reduced circulation is also a characteristic of hibernating mammals. It is quite impossible to count the rapid heartbeats of an active bat, but in semitorpid individuals it is very slow. The hearts of the little ground squirrels of the prairie states beat 30 times as fast at their spring awakening. If a toe of a winter sleeper, mouse or a bat, is cut off during hibernation, little bleeding occurs. This is another proof of the very slow and sluggish circulation common to all true hibernators.

The Hibernation Period

With the approach of cool weather in the northern states and the desiccating winds of the West, hibernators go into shelter. Immediately prior to the winter sleep, the animals appear to fast and their alimentary tracts become empty. If well-fed bats with full stomachs are placed in cold quarters with the approach of the dormant period, they almost invariably fail to become torpid, and usually die within a few days. Alaskan guides state that bears gorge themselves on wild cranberries just before hibernation and purge out their intestines until they are clean as though washed with soap and water.

Western ground squirrels of the United States make elaborate chambers well below the frost line, in contrast with the common eastern chipmunk that stores quantities of food, and is often up and about in the severest midwinter weather. Woodchucks desert their meadow burrows for snug tunnels in the nearby woods. Not all the hibernators go below ground or resort to caves. Black bears have been found sleeping on the open floors of spruce swamps, protected only by surrounding trees. More often they select large hollow stumps or dense windfalls as a winter retreat.

The length of the hibernation period is dependent on a number of factors, including the latitude and weather Ground squirrels have been known to hibernate 33 weeks in the state of Washington. Woodchucks may remain in their winter quarters for five months or longer. Bats have been recorded hibernating for seven months.

The hibernating quarters are unusually small and cramped, which may account for the customary position assumed by the winter sleepers. They roll into a ball, the nose touching the chest or belly. The feet are brought close together, the limbs are rigid, and the tail is laid to one side, over the head and down the spine. The eyes and ears are tightly closed, and the animals appear to be frozen into a tight ball. Bats cling to the walls and ceiling of caves, sometimes far back in the innermost recesses. When abundant, they often hang in large clusters numbering hundreds.

The Spring Emergence

The long winter sleep may end because of several influencing factors. Warmer temperatures are probably the main stimulus to awakening, for little food seems to be eaten even when it is available. The early February thaws and melting snows show the zig-zag tracks of the skunk wandering over the fields. Mating occurs at this early season, and then the skunk may return to its winter retreat for another week or two. Long before the brown buds of the pussy willows burst their sheaths or the first grackles and redwings proclaim spring, the woodchuck is abroad. The urge to mate brings it from the dark

The jumping mouse is a true hibernator. During its long winter sleep its breathing becomes barely perceptible, its heart slows down, and its body temperature approaches that of the surrounding environment

ground after which it retires again to the slumber chambers. Usually, however, animals remain active once they have left the hibernating den.

If one brings a dormant woodchuck from its winter quarters into a warm room, it becomes active in less than an hour. Immediately respiration increases, the eyes attempt to open, and the forepaws make feeble movements. After a few minutes normal respiration is restored and the animal struggles to stand upright. Shortly, violent shivering occurs,

the eyes open, and the hind legs function. With this "return to life" the temperature once more approximates normal. In the short space of an hour, the temperature may rise 60° F.

Such profound changes may be observed only in the true hibernators. The light sleepers (bears, skunks, racoons) maintain a relatively high temperature even when asleep for long periods and recover from their semidormant condition to normal within a few minutes.

Since the confirmed hibernators store no food other than the layer of fat on their bodies, one might expect this to be used up during the quiescent period of winter. The little thirteen-striped ground squirrel of the Middle West, common to every farm, spends a long period underground. From October to March it hibernates beneath the corn and wheat stubble. Fat and sleek in the fall, it has lost fully 40 percent of its weight by late winter. Woodchucks likewise lose from a third to nearly half of their fall weight during their four or five months of sleep.

Summer Sleep

In hot and dry countries many animals pass the hottest season in a torpid condition. This condition known as *aestivation*, seems to have evolved as a means of escape from the recurrent shortage of food brought about by drought, and to maintain the body's moisture. Thus the famous lung fish of Africa becomes encased in a hard, dry, earthen cell, while Australian frogs also repair to the dried stream and lake bottoms during periods of drought. There they pass into a comatose condition until rains again flood the land. In the western United States, the ripening grains are followed by long periods of drought. Since little food and moisture is available, the ground squirrels disappear into their tunnels in early July, not appearing above ground until the following February. The little striped chipmunk of the eastern United States, also disappears during the late summer. Some suspect the stripers are dormant, but their retirement underground probably can be attributed to family duties, for the woods swarm with young chipmunks following this period.

The Mystery of Hibernation

Many questions about hibernation still baffle scientists. Much has been learned about the physiology of the hibernating animal under laboratory conditions which attempt to simulate the animal's habitat, but it is almost impossible to match all the factors which a hibernator meets under natural conditions. Why do some hibernators actually become more active as the fall nights grow colder?

There is a great deal to be learned regarding the winter sleep of all animals. Much can be discovered by the young naturalist with little previous training but with an inherent interest and curiosity. The teeming millions of ground squirrels that inhabit almost every northern state from coast to coast offer a fertile field for investigation. When do they disappear in the fall? What are the dates of emergence in the spring? Do the young precede or follow the adults into the ground? Is there any winter activity of various species during the mild spells? If storage of food is practiced, does this in any way affect the winter activity? These are but a few of the questions which await solution for numerous species. Any one of the many rodent hibernators would repay careful study. Little is known, other than in a general way, of the hibernating sites of turtles, frogs, and snakes. It is known that some congregate in large numbers, but for what purpose is quite unknown. Any inquisitive schoolboy with an interest in natural history can make a worthwhile contribution to our knowledge of the subject. (*See also Winter: The Ways of Wildlife in Winter*)

—W.J.H., Jr.

Recommended Reading

Field Book of Animals in Winter—Ann Haven Morgan. G.P. Putnam's Sons, New York.
Mammalian Hibernation—Edited by Charles P. Lyman and Albert R. Dawe. (Proceedings of the First International Symposium on Natural Mammalian Hibernation, May 13–15, 1959). Bulletin of the Museum of Comparative Zoology at Harvard College, Cambridge, Massachusetts.
Winter Sleeping Wildlife—Will Barker. Harper & Brothers, New York.

Hibernation of Birds

From the time of Aristotle (384–322 B.C.), if not earlier, men have speculated on bird hibernation. Two thousand years later, Edmund C. Jaeger, Professor

The yellow-bellied marmot spends much of its life asleep. During hibernation it lives only on stored body fats and may lose as much as 40 percent of its weight before it awakens

The bear spends the winter in a den but does not hibernate

Richardson's ground squirrel hibernates underground for seven or eight months of the year

Hanging head downward, a little brown bat hibernates in a cave. Many species of bats are true hibernators

in Riverside College, California, recorded the first scientifically observed instance of the trait. The bird involved, a poor-will, was found in the Chuckawalla Mountains, snuggled in the same rocky cavity during three winters. In the winter of 1947-48 Professor Jaeger studied the hibernating bird over a period of 85 days. It was profoundly torpid and gave little response to handling; its body temperature was about 30 percent below normal and it lost weight throughout the time of observation—all typical indications of a true hibernating state. The poor-will was photographed and was seen by other people.

Reviewing the past literature on bird torpidity in 1947, one could find no definite evidence that any bird can survive a full season of genuine hibernation. That gap in knowledge has been filled and one may expect that studies stimulated by Professor Jaeger's findings will greatly increase knowledge in this field.

Some of the earlier, unverified accounts of bird hibernation pertain to relatives of the poor-will. These include the North American whip-poor-will, the Australian frogmouth, and representatives of the closely placed order containing the swifts and hummingbirds. Alexander Wilson, sometimes called the Father of American Ornithology, described torpidity in a ruby-throated hummingbird, lasting half a day, and various later authors have recorded torpidity among captive hummingbirds observed to persist up to a maximum of 20 hours. The common chimney swift is known to become torpid and it has reliably been recorded as being found in chimneys, or even emerging from them in northern localities during the winter. These observations were not scientifically followed up, nor was that of Wilson C. Hanna on the white-throated swift. He found several of these birds numb in a cliff crevice in the Slover Mountains, California, in January 1913. Kept in a room for some hours, they revived, and when released, flew away. These swifts are fond of high places which are not readily visited in winter, and that may explain why Hanna learned no more about their dormancy. If full advantage could have been taken of this opportunity, he, also a Californian, might have been the first to demonstrate bird hibernation.

The published hibernation lore on birds is scattered pretty well throughout the avian family tree. The alleged participants are largely of the Old World, but they include also a fair number of North American species—the turkey vulture, willow ptarmigan, Virginia rail, sora, Carolina parakeet, bank, barn, and cliff swallows, purple martin, and bluebird. Verification seems unlikely for most of these, but hibernation would have been most probable for the parakeet, now apparently extinct and unavailable for investigation.

Bird hibernation, attributed to swallows more than to any other group of birds, has been mentioned during all periods of the 2,000-year record. If people preserve the same attitude toward these disclosures that they take toward other natural history evidence, they must credit some of the reports of swallows being found torpid in dry places. These accounts have the authority of men reputable in every way and are as credible as any unusual thing one has not seen with his own eyes. Thus when the observation of Sir John McNeill and Sir Henry Rawlinson appears in *Nature*, the leading scientific magazine of the British Empire, that they found hundreds of swallows dormant in burrows in Persia, one must believe them. Both were men of the highest repute, knighted by their government.

Considering the tales of swallows hibernating in mud or under water, our knowledge of the physiology of these birds suggests that these stories can hardly be true. Yet they are the most numerous of all of the accounts of hibernation and some of them, alleging the drawing forth of swallows in the nets of fishermen, have been supported by affidavits, sometimes of numerous asserted eyewitnesses; however, that birds so active as swallows could dive beneath water and become torpid in a twinkling, or that they could live entirely shut off from air, is wholly incredible.

It is such legends that gave the whole mass of bird-hibernation lore a bad name, and led one American writer to say that intelligent men abandoned the belief a century ago. In fact the subject became one that some biologists would not consider in the belief that to do so would jeopardize their reputations for scientific probity. However, in the limitless realm of biology, when men of honor assert that something has been observed, it will not do to say, "I don't believe it," or even, "I fear you are mistaken." Marvels everywhere exist and new ones are ever being revealed. Mere torpidity in birds is well known and now that genuine hibernation has been demonstrated, students may set to work at broadening knowledge in this field without fear that their justly-prized standing as men of science may be jeopardized. For this welcome change, Professor Jaeger must be hailed not only as a discoverer but also as an emancipator.   —W.L.M.

Recommended Reading

Does the Poor-Will Hibernate?—Edmund C. Jaeger. *The Condor*, January—February 1948. **Further Observations on The Hibernation of The Poor-Will**—Edmund C. Jaeger. *The Condor*, May—June 1949.

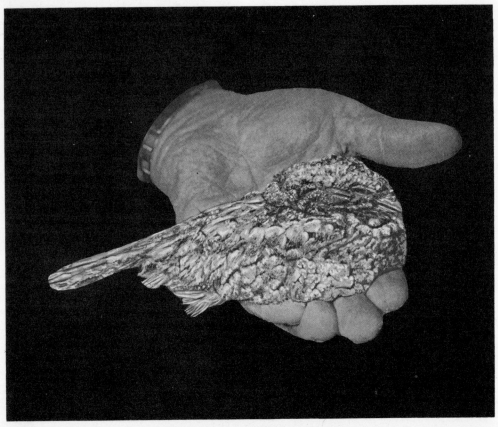

A dormant hand-held poor-will

HICKORY

Shagbark Hickory

Other Common Names—Hickory, shellbark hickory

Scientific Name—*Carya ovata*

Family—Juglandaceae (walnut family)

Range—Florida to eastern Texas, north to southern Maine, southern Quebec and Ontario, central Michigan, Wisconsin, southern Minnesota, and southern Nebraska

Habitat—Rich woods, bottoms, gentle slopes or stream margins

Leaves—Compound, 8 to 20 (usually 12 to 14) inches long, with 5 (rarely 7) finely-toothed leaflets set very close to the stem, the outer 3 of noticeably large size. Leaves grow alternately on the twigs (unlike those of ash, which are opposite)

Bark—Fairly smooth and grayish when young, soon becoming irregular and splitting with age, the ends of the strips peeling up in characteristic fashion

Flowers—Small, rusty female flowers are inconspicuous beside bunches of drooping male catkins, four to five inches long, which appear about May as the new leaves unfurl

Fruit—Thick-hulled, nearly spherical, usually 1½ to 2 inches across. Splitting into four parts to release a hard, creamy-shelled nut. Borne singly or in twos and threes; ripening in the fall

Shagbark hickory

The shagbark hickory is a well-known member of the hickory group, which includes about 10 species in North America, most of them trees of the eastern and central United States. Its unique bark, which makes identification of the more mature trees easy, is equaled only by that of the big shellbark hickory, *Carya laciniosa,* of the Midwest, a tree with somewhat larger leaves and bigger fruits.

The qualities of hickory wood—heavy, hard, stiff-but-springy, durable, and highly shock-resistant—make it virtually unsurpassed for tool handles and gymnastic equipment. It is also used for fuel and for smoking meats. Very large trees are rare and the height is seldom over 75 feet. Occasionally trees 120 feet or more high, with trunks 30 inches in diameter, are found.

Because of the desirability of the wood for lumber, most hickories, especially this one, have probably been subjected to more selective cutting than other trees within their range. Observations and accounts of fully developed woodlands such as the pioneers found suggest that this and some other hickories were considerably more numerous than they are now.

Other common hickories include such species as mockernut hickory, *Carya alba,* much like the shagbark; the pignut hickory, *C. glabra;* the pecan, *C. illinoensis;* a semiaquatic water hickory of southern distribution, *C. aquatica;* and a rather distinctive species—with narrow leaflets, thin, mustard yellow winter buds, and finned nuts—called the bitternut hickory, *C. cordiformis.* A person unfamiliar with this last-named species might mistake it for a walnut, but the number of rather tough leaflets—usually seven to nine, with the largest ones on the outer half of the leaf—are positive marks of identification.

In spring the tasseled catkins of hickories are quite prominent on the male trees and, along with oak catkins and other tree blossoms, produce a quantity of pollen. Most hickories are attractive shade trees and have edible nuts. —M.B.

HOAR-FROST *(See under Frost)*

HOLLY

The southeastern United States is the main home of the holly family, the Aquifoliaceae. The best known is the American holly, *Ilex opaca*, with its shiny, spine-edged leaves that remain on the tree far into the winter, even after the snow has fallen, and contrast strongly with the brilliant red berries. None of the other hollies are so noticeably spiny; some have black berries, and are not large trees, but more shrublike.

The sweet gallberry, *Ilex coriacea*, a southern swampland species, has leaves that are leathery and soft pulpy fruits that are said to be edible. The yaupon, *Ilex vomitoria*, the leaves of which were used for tea and as an emetic by the Indians and pioneers, is similar; it has red berries and leaves that are pale green below and without hair.

Several hollies are called winterberries. They are deciduous, not evergreen, and lose their leaves in the fall. The berries are red or yellow, depending on the species. They are more northern than the other hollies, one species, *Ilex verticillata*, ranging north to Newfoundland.

The inkberry, *Ilex glabra*, growing in low, sandy soils from Nova Scotia to Florida, is an evergreen holly with toothed leaves and shiny black berries.

A second genera—*Nemopanthus*—contains a single species, the mountain holly, or catberry, *Nemopanthus mucronata*, that grows in damp woods, thickets, and swamps from Newfoundland east to Minnesota and south to

American holly

Nova Scotia, Illinois, Ohio, Indiana, upland Virginia, and West Virginia.
—G.B.S.

American Holly
Other Common Names—Christmas holly, white holly
Scientific Name—*Ilex opaca*
Family—Aquifoliaceae (holly family)
Range—Florida to Texas and north to eastern Massachusetts, southeastern New York, eastern Pennsylvania, West Virginia, southern Ohio, northern Kentucky, southern Illinois, southeastern Missouri, and Oklahoma
Habitat—Moist woodlands
Leaves—Mostly two to three inches long, oval, stiff, and leathery, with numerous needle-sharp points along the edges. Paler beneath, and shed in the spring after about three years
Bark—Moderately smooth, varying from dark to pale smoky-gray. In beach areas, often almost white and spotted with varicolored lichens
Flowers—Inconspicuous little sprays of

greenish-white, four-petalled blossoms that appear in late spring; male and female flowers on separate trees

Fruit—Plump, red, poisonous berries about one-fourth inch in diameter that ripen in autumn and stay on through the winter, when they are much eaten by birds

American holly is the state tree of Delaware. It is so widely used as a Christmas decoration that few people, except those who raise it commercially or people who live where it is abundant, think of it as a tree. Although this particular species grows in various situations in the South, as one travels northward it is found more frequently near the seashore in sandy-loamy soils; it even grows on barrier beach islands off the coast of New Jersey, where it is approaching the northern limit of its range.

The American holly is a medium-sized tree, the usual maximum being a height of about 40 to 50 feet with a trunk a foot or two in diameter. Musical instruments, especially organ and piano keys, and other special items are made from the wood. With these uses claiming marketable-sized trees and the holiday collection and sale of berry-laden branches further depleting the holly, the tree is in need of protection. To add to the manmade pressure on the species, this native holly is a slow-growing tree. But fortunately it has the advantage, when established directly on the coast, of flourishing in an oceanic climate, which limits or adversely affects many other plants.   —M.H.B.

HOMING
The Homing of Birds

The marvelous homing faculty of birds has been known to mankind for ages. The Greeks referred to it 2,500 years ago. Primitive man makes use of it as, for example, in the South Sea Islands, where frigate birds are used to carry messages. The modern interest in bird migration, however, has led to a scientific investigation of the homing birds.

Bird migration would be impossible without the homing faculty. Many birds use a different route in the fall migration than in the spring, and still they return to the same garden, field, or lake that they had left the year before. Of course, bird migration (*see under Migration: Secrets of Migration*) is frequently a flight toward an unknown destination (fall flight of young birds), while homing is always a flight toward a known goal.

There has been some confusion of terms. What is homing? Homing is the ability to return to a known goal over an at least partially unknown flight route. The expression "homing instinct" has frequently been used for this phenomenon, but although there is no objection to a judicious use of the term *instinct*, one must carefully distinguish between, first, the inner urge that impels the bird to fly back to its home, and, second, the sense that enables the bird to return from an unknown country to its home.

If a bird fails to return, that is no proof that it lacks the homing sense; it may only lack the urge to home. This is well illustrated by an experiment. Only eight percent of a group of female starlings that had been trapped on nests without eggs returned, while 35 percent of the females that were trapped from nests with eggs or young came back.

Anyone who has watched a bird go to its nest has probably noticed how it almost always follows the same route. It is in familiar surroundings and orients itself by vision and habit, much the same way as people move around in their homes. This is called *local orientation*. There are no difficulties connected with understanding local orientation. The real problem is the distant orientation: How do birds find their way through unfamiliar surroundings, and how do they get to goals with which they have no direct connection through known sense organs (sight, etc.)?

It was evident that experiments were

the only hope of finding an answer to these questions. Domesticated homing pigeons were the first birds used for such studies, but this species is, in fact, rather badly suited for homing investigations, because the wild rock dove, *Columba livia,* the ancestor of the domestic homing pigeon, is a nonmigratory bird and has only weakly developed homing faculties. Ever since this was discovered, wild birds have been given the preference over homing pigeons in all experimental studies on homing.

Every species of wild bird that has been investigated has shown that it possessed the homing faculty, at least to some extent. Some seabirds (man-o'-war birds, terns, and gulls), and wrynecks, cowbirds, starlings, and swallows, as well as other migratory birds, have it particularly well developed. Sedentary birds, such as house sparrows, have it only weakly, but it is never quite absent. Almost every issue of the scientific bird journals records a few new instances of amazing homing flights.

Two American scientists were the first to do serious work on homing with live birds. In 1910 they captured noddies, *Anous stolidus,* and sooty terns, *Sterna anaethetus,* on the Tortugas Keys between Florida and Cuba, then transported them by steamer to various parts of the Atlantic Coast of the eastern states or the Gulf Coast of the southern states.

Transportation was slow and the feeding of the birds was difficult. The result was that in their early experiments a great many birds were released in a weakened condition and very few birds returned. The results of their last experiment (in 1913), after most of the technical difficulties had been overcome, are given in Table 1 (second transport from Bird Key to Galveston).

The fastest bird to return from 585 miles was back at its nest after 3 days and 22½ hours, and from 855 miles after 6 days and 2 hours. Such experiments can be repeated with a modern fast means of transportation such as airplanes, as has been successfully done in Germany by Dircksen.

These experiments confirm what is already known by observation about the amazing homing faculties of seabirds. Many of them, including the young birds of the year, leave their home island after the breeding season and scatter during the winter over thousands of miles of open ocean. But at the beginning of the next breeding season they seem to have found their way back to the tiny little spot in the wide expanse of sea.

The greater shearwater, *Puffinus gravis,* nests on Tristan da Cunha Island, 37° south of the equator, 1,600 miles west of Africa; but in the southern winter—the North American summer—it is all along the Atlantic shores as far as Greenland and the Arctic Circle. In Robert Cushman Murphy's *Oceanic Birds of South America* similar wanderings are described for many species.

The most important experiments carried out in other early years were those by W. Ruppell on starlings in Germany. The starling was chosen because it is a common and robust bird, and because the return of individuals of this species,

The sooty tern was one of the first birds to be used in homing experiments

TABLE I (after Watson and Lashley)

Distance from Bird Key (in miles)	No. of birds released	Returned
418	2 Noddies	None
585	6 Sooties, 4 Noddies	5 Sooties, 3 Noddies
720	2 Noddies	2 Noddies
855	6 Sooties, 4 Noddies	2 Sooties, 1 Noddy
Total	12 Noddies 12 Sooties	6 Noddies (= 50%) 7 Sooties (= 58.4%)

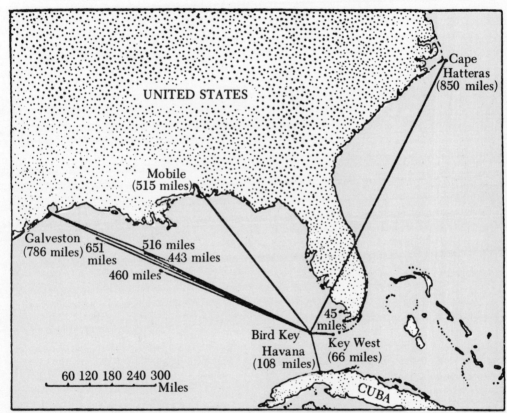

The distances and directions from which sooty and noddy terns returned to Bird Key, Florida, in experiments conducted on homing

which nests in artificial boxes, can be observed rather easily. In order to improve the results, the ordinary nesting boxes can be replaced by those that automatically trap the bird after its return.

Technique of the Experiment

The bird is caught in the evening, if it is to be transported long distances by rail, otherwise in the morning. It is banded and, if possible, stained with a conspicuous dye so that it can be recognized among other members of the species. At least a dozen birds should be used at each experiment, to reduce accidental errors. The birds are packed in individual boxes and shipped as speedily as possible by train or airplane. At the point of release, the exact time is recorded by the collaborator, who, if possible, should have some knowledge of

TABLE II

RETURNING STARLINGS IN 1935

Experiment	Number of shipped birds			Caught after return		
	♂	♀	Total	♂	♀	Total
Winsen-Berlin 171 miles	7	15	22	85.7%	40%	12 = 54.5%
Winsen-Malmœ 190 miles	12	9	21	58.4%	33.3%	10 = 47.6%
Scheessel-Malmœ 219 miles	20	22	42	45%	54.5%	21 = 50%
Malmœ (Total)	32	31	63	50%	48.4%	31 = 49.2%
Winsen-Gleiwitz 417 miles	2	0	2	100%		2 = 100%
Scheessel-Gleiwitz 439 miles	4	6	10	75%	66.7%	7 = 70%
Gleiwitz (Total)	6	6	12	83.3%	66.7%	9 = 75%
Total in 1935	45	52	97	60%	48.1%	52 = 53.6%

handling birds. By far the most important factor for the success of the experiment is the careful inspection of the home area.

Many birds are considerably delayed in their homing and it may require 10 days to 2 weeks before they return. Very few birds return to the original box, because this has frequently been occupied in the meantime by some other bird. They usually settle within a couple of hundred feet from the original nest box, but if there is none available they may settle half a mile or a mile away. All this indicates clearly that the most careful and constant surveillance of the home area is the key to the success of such experiments.

In 1934 a total of 353 starlings were released for 31 different home bases. About 120 birds (or 34 percent) returned. It was found that it was unsatisfactory to work with too many collaborators, many of whom could devote but little time to the observation of the birds. The experiment was therefore repeated in 1935 on a smaller scale, but much

more efficiently. Table 2 illustrates the results.

These results show that the extensive homing flight across water of the Malmoe starling had little or no effect on its ability to return. It also shows that returns from greater distances (439 miles) are not less successful than those from smaller distances; in fact, they seem to be more successful.

Again, as in previous experiments, fewer females returned than males, although the 1935 experiments were carried out during the breeding season. This indicates that the ties to the home are not so close in the female as in the male, and that 60 percent (of the returning males) must be considered the minimum number for returns of the starling. These figures include only those birds that were caught after their return to the original home colony. In addition to these, several birds were observed within half a mile of the colony. This justifies the supposition that every bird returns to the home district, except those killed by enemies or bad weather. There is no correlation between the success of a particular shipment and the geographical position of the point of release in relation to the home goal. Flights in the direction of the migration route are by no means more successful than those crosswise to it.

Speed of Flight

The maximum daily distance covered by the homing starling is 75 miles. Thus, if the distance between the point of release and home is between 75 and 150 miles, the first birds will arrive on the second day; if the distance is between 375 and 450 miles, the first birds will arrive on the sixth day. This conflicts with the results of homing pigeon races, where birds from great distances return proportionately very much later than those from shorter distances. The "speed limit" of starlings is rather low; being 75 miles per day; it is much higher (250 miles per day) for barn swallows, provided the weather is good. Swallows are much more influenced by poor weather than starlings. Since no observer has the time to watch for returning birds from dawn to dusk, the actual return times are not correct unless automatic traps are used.

In both the 1934 and 1935 homing experiments in Germany a single bird was found dead between the point of release and home, and in both cases it was within a few miles of the direct flight line between the two points. This is by far the strongest evidence for the suppositon that the birds return in a straight line.

Preliminary experiments with swallows showed that they were still better homers than starlings. Of 7 barn swallows, *Hirundo rustica*, sent by airmail to England (430 miles away), 5 (or 71.4 percent) returned, 3 of them within less than a week; of 6 house martins released at Gleiwitz (450 miles from home), not less than 5 (or 83.3 percent) returned to the vicinity of their colony. A shipment of European house martins to England,

was, however, less successful.

Nobody who has read the discussion up to this point will have any doubt that birds have a real homing faculty, an ability that goes much beyond any similar capacity existing in mankind. It is the natural thing to ask now: "What is the mechanism that controls this ability?" This is a question that many investigators have attempted to answer. It is interesting and revealing to present a short survey of the more plausible theories that have been advanced to explain the homing sense, although none of these theories gives a really satisfactory explanation. The experiments carried out in recent years have merely served to disprove the older theories, not to strengthen any of them.

The oldest and probably most widely accepted theory was the visual orientation theory. According to this theory, homing is a matter of memory and random searching. On familiar ground the bird follows a series of landmarks known to it, until it reaches its goal; on unfamiliar ground it wanders around until it picks up a familiar sight. In other words, homing is accomplished by a trial-and-error method. There are numerous objections to this theory. If the return from a strange region is simply a matter of chance, and if the birds fly around in wide spirals, one should expect that the time required for the return would increase in a geometrical proportion to the flight distance. Ruppell's experiments in Germany have, however, shown that the flight time increases in an algebraic relation to the flight distance. A bird released at 500 miles distance will require only 5 times, but not 25 times, as long as one released at 100 miles. Furthermore, the two birds found dead were almost exactly on the theoretical flight line. And what is also important, many experimenters who have released such homing birds have observed that they did not scatter toward all the points of the compass, but that the majority of the birds at once started in the right direction, as if guided by some invisible force (*See under Animal: Navigation of Animals*).

The Retracing Theory

This theory has been formulated by the French investigator, Reynaud, as follows: "The instinct of distance orientation is the ability of birds to retrace the way on which they have come." This theory postulates that birds have a special organ, for example, the semicircular canals, that registers every turn on the road of transport, and also a very fine memory that enables the bird to remember the exact sequence of all the turns and the duration of the straight stretches in between.

As attractive as this theory might be, it does not hold. First of all, it is practically impossible for a passively moved bird to register where the turns are, how sharp they are, and how long they last. And in order for them to be fixed in the memory, the transport would probably have to be repeated many times. The most striking proof against the retracing theory is, however, the triangle experiment. Suppose there are the three towns A, B, and C forming the corners of an equilateral triangle. Twenty starlings are taken from A, and transported to B; then 10 are retained in B, the remaining 10 are carried to C. The 20 birds are now released at B and C at the same moment. According to the retracing theory, it should take the starlings released at C twice as long to get home to A as the starlings released at B, because they have to fly via B. Actual experiments in Germany proved that the starlings released at B and at C arrived home at A at the same time, thus upsetting a fine theory.

Knowledge of Geographical Position Theory

This theory starts with the same basic assumption as the last—that the bird can register and memorize the road of transportation—but with the result that it always knows its geographic position in regard to its home. After the release the bird will at once fly directly toward its home. Just as, let us say, a person in a strange city, sightseeing for hours, keeps track of all changes of direction and finally returns to the hotel on a straight line.

To disprove this theory, two darkened cages with starlings were carried the 93 miles from a German village to Berlin. One of the two cages was mounted on a phonograph disc and rotated on it during the entire railroad journey, making a total of about 5,000 rotations. The slightest error in the recording of these turns would have meant a return flight in the wrong direction. Still these birds returned nearly 100 percent, and, in fact, quicker than the control birds transported under normal conditions. And Professor Exner in Vienna chloroformed some homing pigeons during the transport from their loft to the point of release. These birds returned home as successfully as untreated pigeons, although they could not possibly have registered the changes of direction of their traveling route while they were unconscious.

The clear result of all these experiments is the realization that, as Exner stated, "the orientation on the return flight does not depend in any way on experiences collected during the transport to the point of release." There must be a continuous stimulation associated with the home, which guides the bird as soon as it is released, even if it was unconscious during the transport. Homing is not a matter of memory or intelligence, but it depends on the faculty to react to some unknown stimulus.

What forces exist on the earth that might guide the homing bird? The entire surface of the earth is a gigantic magnetic field. Lines of equal declination and of equal inclination form on the map a net just like the meridians and parallels. Just as there is an absolute zero point of geographical position on

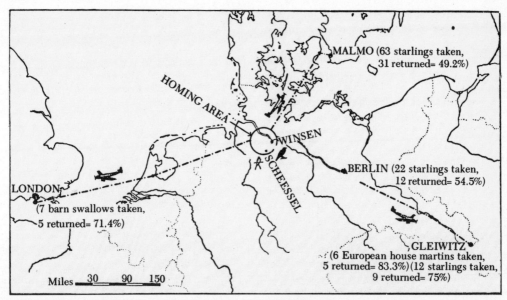

Experiments showed that barn swallows and European house martins were better homers than starlings

the earth (where the meridian of Greenwich crosses the equator), the bird's home might constitute such a magnetic zero point to which it desires to return, if removed.

There are a great many objections to this theory, of which the most important is that no "magnetic sense" organ has yet been found in the bird. Furthermore, earth magnetism is a very unstable force that changes annually and even seasonally. The vast quantities of steel used in the construction of big cities must cause tremendous magnetic disturbances, and yet birds released in the middle of railroad yards have returned home very successfully. However, only a well-planned experiment can finally dispose of this theory. Suppose two groups of starlings are sent on the home journey,

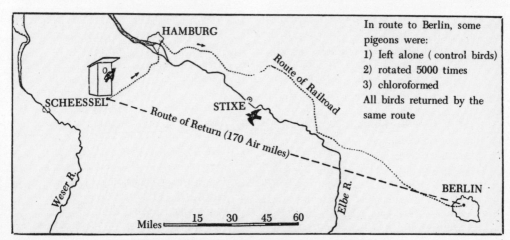

German experiments showed that homing accuracy does not depend on experience gathered during transport to point of release

the experimentals with small magnets tied to the body, and the controls without them. If the experimentals fail to return, it would be fairly convincing proof that the earth's magnetic field guides the bird to its home . . . .

It seems as if the bird were tied to its home with an invisible rubber band and that, no matter what is done with it, it will be pulled back. It was recently suggested that perhaps from every point on the surface of the earth emanate specific radiations, like the waves of a radio station, and that the birds react to these "home rays." This is an attractive theory, but nobody has found any evidence for the existence of such rays, nor has any receiving organ—that is, a specific sense organ— been found in the body of the bird. The frequently heard statement that radio stations were influencing the return of homing pigeons has never been substantiated.

There is no reason to give up hope of a solution. Many scientific problems of the past seemed hopelessly difficult, but patient investigators finally found the answers. The study of homing is a promising field for the enthusiastic bird student. Of the many unsolved problems, a few are: What is the difference between the homing faculty of migratory and sedentary species? What are the homing differences between males and females, between adults and immatures? What are the differences in the return ratio in the different seasons of the year? What are the greatest distances from which birds home, and what differences are there between the homing from small and great distances? Is homing influenced by temporary captivity? Is homing influenced by the earth's magnetism or by radio waves?

To investigate birds of various families in accordance with these questions will produce much valuable material and may provide the key to unlocking the secret of homing.   —E.M.

HONEY (*See under Bee: Honeybee*)

HORNED ANIMALS

The horned animals are classified in two groups. One is the deer family, or Cervidae, hoofed animals with antlers that are shed every year. This includes elk, deer, moose, and caribou, all of which also chew their cuds. The other group is the Bovidae family—animals with hollow horns that are never shed— the bison, goats, musk-ox, and sheep. The pronghorn, of the Antilocapridae family is an exception—it has hollow horns that it sheds each year. (*See under Mammal*)

HORNED POUT (*See Catfish under Fish: Common Freshwater Fishes of North America*)

HORNET

Hornets are stinging insects of the family Vespidae, order Hymenoptera (ants, bees, wasps, and sawflies). Hornets are wasps (*see Wasp*), and the most familiar North American one is the bald-faced, or white-faced, hornet, *Vespula (Dolichovespula) maculata*. Its large size, black-and-white markings, and formidable sting have made it well known to all who hunt, fish, or go birdwatching in country places where it builds its gray, football-sized, paper nest in trees or shrubbery.

Another so-called hornet is the European hornet, introduced accidentally into the New York City area about 1850, and now spread as far south as North Carolina. It is large, reddish-brown, with dull yellow markings. Because it strips bark, with which it builds its paper nest, from some ornamental shrubs, or trees, its accidental introduction has not been considered favorable, even though it preys on certain other insects (*See under Insect: Predators and Parasites*). The nests are usually built in sheltered places in buildings, in hollow trees, and under overhanging rocks. Frank M. Lutz, the former entomologist of the American Museum of Natural History, wrote that this is the only true hornet in America.

Hornet's nest

Bald-faced hornet

Flowers — Snow white blossoms speckled with pink and yellow
Fruit — Mahogany-colored nuts encased in large prickly burs. The fruit is edible if well cooked

The so-called field hornet, another wasp, is more often called a yellow jacket (*See under Yellow Jacket*).

Hornets, like all wasps, are predatory, killing other insects by biting, and taking chunks of flesh back to the hive to feed to the larvae in the comb cells. Most of the young will also take carrion. Adults feed only on liquids, either flower nectar or juices of insects and of rotting or bruised fruit.

The American bald-faced, or paper, hornet chews and partially digests wood fibers to make a nest-building material that resembles pulped cardboard. The nest is begun as a comb dangling from a branch on one column, but it is soon enveloped by a spherical, paper covering, which serves as an outer, protective shell.   —G.B.S.

HORSE CHESTNUT
Other Common Names — Buckeye
Scientific Name — *Aesculus hippocastanum*
Family — Hippocastanaceae (buckeye family)
Range — Native to Balkan Peninsula
Habitat — Introduced from Europe and widely planted as a shade tree
Leaves — Large compound leaves with seven "heavy-ended," coarsely toothed leaflets
Bark — Irregularly flaky, grayish-brown on mature trees

Because of its large leaves and great beauty when blooming, the horse chestnut, native of southeastern Europe, has been employed by man as an ornamental tree throughout much of Europe, Great Britain, and the United States. Since its introduction to North America in 1746 the horse chestnut has become so increasingly common as a shade tree that most Americans are unfamiliar with its native relatives. A member of the buckeye family, most commonly found in the tropical regions of the Old World, the horse chestnut nevertheless has 10 closely related species that are native to the United States. Many of these are valuable timber trees.

Longfellow's poem about a village blacksmith whose forge was "under a spreading chestnut tree," refers to the European species that we call horse chestnut. The association of the tree with a blacksmith's trade in this poem is oddly appropriate because the name horse chestnut is probably derived from the shape of the leaf scars that appear on the stout twigs and are shaped much like the underside of a horse's hoof.

As a group the buckeyes are distinguished by their long, palmate leaves that sometimes attain a width of 12 inches, by large mahogany-colored, well-polished nuts enclosed in a thick, often prickly husk, and, in the winter months, by deep brown, sticky, terminal buds. Several shrublike forms, as well as the typical trees of the midwestern and southern states, are included in the

The showy flowers of the horse-chestnut tree bloom in early spring

buckeye family. The term *buckeye* refers to the pale oval at the top of the ripe nut. It resembles the eye of a deer.

The horse chestnut blooms in early spring, at which time it is covered with panicles of peppermint-pink and white blossoms. In fall the large fruit cases open, and the ripened nuts fall to the ground. The fruit is generally toxic to man and livestock; however, if well-cooked over fire, horse chestnuts become edible.

Ohio buckeye, *Aesculus glabra*, and the sweet buckeye, *Aesculus octandra*, are the two largest native species. Both of these trees are found chiefly in a large south-central area that spans the Mississippi basin. Both, along with the horse chestnut, may attain a height of 75 feet, with a trunk diameter of 2 feet or more, although these figures are well beyond the average dimensions. The California buckeye, *Aesculus californica*, is confined to the western coast and closely resembles the other species.

Because of the toxic nature of their fruit and the disagreeable odor emitted from the blossoms of many buckeyes, the horse chestnut's native relatives have been much reduced in numbers by cutting. (*See also Buckeye*)

—G.A.B.

HORSESHOE CRAB

Horseshoe crabs, or king crabs, are not true crabs but are primitive marine arthropods more closely related to the **spiders and scorpions than to crabs (***See under Arthropod***).** Although formidable looking, they are harmless.

During the late spring and early summer, as the waters from the Gulf of Mexico to Maine become progressively warmer, horseshoe crabs migrate from the deeper bay waters to the land to mate. They move across the bottom with an ungainly gait or swim gracefully on their backs at the surface of the water as they approach the shoreline at high-water time. Usually the males precede the females to the beach, where they patrol the shallow water, seemingly anticipating the arrival of their mates. Few females reach the beach unattended after passing through this vigilant stag line.

The female makes her way with the male to the beach at the water's edge. It is picturesque under a full moon to see the dark shells of hundreds of mating animals at the water's edge, surrounded by the glistening frothy foam of the surf. Each female scoops a shallow nest out of the sand and in this she deposits a clutch of several hundred eggs. The gentle churning of the water over the eggs insures fertilization. The pair moves on and sand is washed over the nest, sealing it until the next high tide a month later. As the tide ebbs, the mating pair takes up another nesting position at a lower level. They make several nests on each spring tide and then return to the mud flats to feed.

Horseshoe crabs instinctively select the highest tides of the month during which to lay their eggs, but the difference in the rise and fall of the tidal water in different localities causes variations in the spawning behavior. Along the Atlantic Coast south of Cape Cod, where there is less than a six-foot difference between high and low tide, the nests are made along the beaches at the high-water line. Where the rise of the water exceeds 10

feet, as in Cape Cod Bay and northward, the spawning areas are not at the highest waterline but are usually lower on the beach. The weather, too, has a marked effect on spawning behavior. For example, during a prevailing northwesterly wind in the Cape May region of Delaware Bay, the horseshoe crabs do not come in to the New Jersey shore to spawn, but remain offshore until it is calm again.

During the breeding season and, later, throughout the spring and summer, the adults wander over the intertidal mud flats in search of food. They are voracious feeders and may be found partially or wholly buried, feeding upon various marine worms and soft-shell clams. Within two weeks after the horseshoe crab's eggs are laid, the shell of each egg splits and lets water into an inner membrane, which becomes inflated like a balloon. If the eggs are dug out of the nest it can be seen that the membrane is transparent and that it provides a wonderful showcase in which to watch the little embryo develop. Now it has room in which to grow. Soon the buds of its limbs grow into legs, which begin to move. The little animal, still within the egg, is now in a constant state of animation busily kicking this way and that, but always it is on its back because it is top-heavy.

In about a month the churning motion of a tide washes away the sand covering the nest and ruptures the membrane. This liberates the tailless larvae, which are now carried down to the mud flats by the tidal currents.

The small creatures crawl and swim about, leading an active life in spite of the fact that they do not need to search for food. Their food, the remnant of the egg yolk, is neatly "packaged" within their digestive tract. When this built-in food supply is used, the animal molts for the first time. After this initial molt the young horseshoe crab has a tail and its body shape fully resembles that of the adult. It now feeds on tiny organisms that live in the ooze that covers the

The horseshoe crab is closely related to scorpions and spiders

surface of the mud flats. The small animal sheds its shell more than once during the first summer and wanders about the flats, feeding on ever larger organisms.

When fall approaches, the small horseshoe crabs stay on the mud flats, burying themselves to escape the cold water and ice, but the parents begin a great exodus to their winter habitat in the deeper waters.

As the years go by the little horseshoe crab grows larger and larger. During early summer, weeks before molting actually occurs, a soft new skin forms underneath the hard outer shell. This new skin is wrinkled and pleated like an accordion. At molting time the forward edge of the horseshoe-shaped shield splits and the animal struggles to emerge from its old shell. The molting animal is aided in its struggles by an internal pressure created by an increased amount of water in its tissue. As it emerges, the pleats unfold and the skin hardens to form the new shell.

With each molt the growing horseshoe crab increases its linear dimensions about 25 percent. It stops molting when it reaches adulthood, but the exact number of years of development prior to adulthood is not known. Nine to eleven years seems a reasonably close estimate, but it may be even longer.

Today there are only two regions in the world where horseshoe crabs may be found. One of these is the coastal waters of Asia from India to Japan, including the waters around Indonesia and the Philippine Islands, where three species have been found. The other region is the Atlantic coastline of North America from Maine to Yucatan. Here there is but one species, *Limulus polyphemus*. This geographical distribution occurred some 60

million years ago when all of the horseshoe crabs left European waters, never to return. The seas where Europe now stands were the center of this dispersal, one group migrating westward, the others eastward.

The horseshoe crab was well known to North American Indians, who sometimes ate them and often used the pointed tail to arm the tips of their fish spears. When the Europeans first came to the New World they were already familiar with the living animal, since the Asiatic species had been imported earlier from the Far East, as a curiosity, along with commodities of trade.

The horseshoe crab, which is more closely allied to the ancient sea scorpions and to modern scorpions and spiders than it is to the true crabs, was at first mistakenly identified as a crustacean by Europeans who called it the king crab. More descriptive are the American names of *horseshoe* or *horsefoot crab* and *horsefeet* as they are called by the fishermen of New Jersey. *Swordtail crab* and *pan crab* have also been used, the latter by the colonial fishermen who used the empty shells to bail out their boats.

The horseshoe crab has also been used in several other ways. Fishermen quarter the egg-laden females for lobster and eel bait, and farmers have fed them to their chickens and hogs. The largest numbers of horseshoe crabs are used to make fertilizer. Although they are steadily decreasing, thousands of these animals are still captured for this purpose along the shores of Delaware Bay in special traps that resemble fish pounds.

Numerous scientific experiments have been performed upon the horseshoe crab. Studies of its heart action, the function of its blood, its nervous system, and its visual sense have received the most attention. Results obtained by studies of these comparatively simply constructed animals have aided biologists in explaining biological mechanisms in more complex animals.

Besides man, many animals prey on the horseshoe crab. In spite of its well-armored appearance any adult left stranded and overturned on a beach by a high tide is subject to the predations of the larger shorebirds and other animals. Its skin has several weak spots on the undersurface of the body and can be easily torn open. The younger, thinner-shelled animals are the most vulnerable. Occasionally the ungainly male spider crab catches and overturns one of these younger animals and makes a meal of it; and other crabs, particularly the blueclaw crab, feed upon horseshoe crabs. However, the greatest loss of life is at the beginning, when saltwater fishes, eels, and

shorebirds follow along after the mating pairs or dig in the sand to feed upon the newly laid eggs or the larvae.

Despite the animals that prey upon the horseshoe crab and upon its eggs, and other conditions that determine its populations, it has survived successfully for more than 300 million years. The test of time has not found it wanting in the ability to meet successfully all situations that threaten its survival—except its destruction by man.　　　—C.N.S., Jr.

HORSETAIL (*See under Club Mosses and Horsetails*)

HOTTENTOT-FIG
Other Common Names — Fig marigold
Scientific Name — *Mesembryanthemum* (*Carpobrotus*) *edule*
Family — Aizoaceae (fig marigold family)
Range — Patagonia to Marin County California; Africa, hot sandy places, sea cliffs
Habitat — Along coasts
Time of Blooming — From April to October

The very large name of this plant simply means *midday flower*, since it opens in the middle of the day. The long stems throw themselves flat on the sands near the coast. The leaves are as long as a finger and they have three sides. They are hard and stiff and the pointed ends are sometimes crimson. The flowers are creamy yellow but turn to pink after a day or two. The plant is always green and is much used to cover bare ground along roadsides and on bluffs and as a protection against erosion and as a sand-binder since the roots hold sand in place.

The Hottentot-fig closely resembles *Mesembryanthemum chilense* (sea fig) but the leaves are longer and brighter green and the flowers larger; three to four inches in diameter. The Hottentot-fig is a native of South Africa and has become naturalized in central and southern California.

Hottentot-fig

HUMMINGBIRD

The approximately 319 species of hummingbirds of the world live only in the western hemisphere, with the greatest concentration of both numbers and species in the Andes Mountains of Colombia, South America. About 15 species nest or appear in North America north of Mexico, and 7 of these are not at all common north of the Mexican border.

The smallest bird in the world is the Cuban bee hummingbird, only 2¼ inches long and weighing about as much as a dime. The largest of the family (Trochilidae) is the South American giant hummingbird, 8½ inches long (*See also under Facts About Birds*).

The most noticeable feature of male hummingbirds, aside from their small size, is the iridescent colors of the gorget, or throat patch. Both sexes of the violet-crowned hummingbird have white below the bill.

Another feature shared by both sexes is the exceptionally long bill with which the birds sip nectar and capture insects and spiders from the tubes of flowers. The feet of the hummingbirds, as with their closest relatives, the swifts, are small and weak; however, they often perch on twigs or on wires. Hummingbirds never walk or hop, but fly even for the shortest distances.

The wings of hummingbirds and swifts differ significantly from those of all other birds, in that the upper arm bones are very short, while the lower arm bones are elongated. Hummingbirds have larger flying muscles in proportion to their weight than those of any other species of birds. The movement of the wings is extremely fast—up to 200 beats a second during courtship flights; 75 beats a second in normal flight; 55 beats a second while hovering. The shoulder girdle is constructed in such a way that hummers can use the upstroke of the wings for propulsion, as well as the downstroke that is the only power stroke for all other birds. Hummers can fly forward, backward, up, down, and, to some extent, sideways (*See under Bird: Bird Flight*).

—G.B.S.

Hummingbird Ways

In *The Naturalist on the River Amazon*, Henry W. Bates says: "Hummingbirds are unlike other birds in their mental qualities. The want of expression in their eyes, the small degree of versatility in their actions, the quickness and precision of their movements, are all so many points of resemblance between them and insects."

In *The Naturalist in La Plata*, W. H. Hudson, the English nature writer, expresses similar views: "It has frequently been remarked that hummingbirds are more like insects than birds in disposition . . . Their aimless attacks on other species approaching or passing near them, even on large birds like hawks and pigeons, is a habit they have in common with many solitary wood-boring bees. They also, like dragonflies and other insects, attack each other, when they come together while feeding. . . .

"Again, like insects, they are undisturbed at the presence of man while feeding, or even when engaged in building and incubation; and like various solitary bees, wasps, etc., they frequently come close to a person walking or standing, to hover suspended in the air within a few inches of his face; and if then struck at they often, insectlike, return to circle round his head. All other birds, even those which display the least versatility, and in districts where man is seldom seen, show as much caution as curiosity in his presence; they recognize in the upright unfamiliar form a living being and a possible enemy."

Many other writers have referred to the extreme pugnacity or quarrelsomeness of hummingbirds. However, before accepting unquestioningly the conclusions of eminent naturalists, the evidence upon which they based their verdicts should be examined.

In recognizing the resemblance between hummingbirds and certain insects

*Rufous hummingbird (top)—adult male (left), immature male (center), female (right);
Allen's hummingbird (middle)—adult male (left), immature male (center), female
(right); broad-tailed hummingbird (bottom)—adult male (left), female (right)*

such as hawkmoths, due consideration should be given to the fact that parallel adaptation to the same method of obtaining food would naturally bring about analogies in both structure and actions. The lack of fear that is cited as evidence of insectlike mentality is certainly well justified by the bird's quickness and alertness, which enable it to maintain its abundance even though only two, four, or occasionally six eggs are laid each year; and the young are subjected to the vicissitudes of an unusually long period of helplessness, and dependence upon the female parent only. This contrasts strongly with the immense potential annual increase by which most insects must compensate for their high death rate.

That the hummingbird is not in fact foolhardy or lacking in judgment is indicated by the observation that a cat seems much more disturbing to it than the near presence of a human being. While their alarm is usually caused by motion rather than form, some hummingbirds show quite as much suspicion of an unfamiliar stationary object, such as a camera, as do many other birds. That hummingbirds are curious and actively interested in their surroundings is undeniable, but it seems strange that this should have been regarded by W. H. Hudson as an evidence of low mentality characteristic of insects.

Resident hummingbirds select certain territories that they defend against other hummingbirds with vigor. The principal difference lies in the persistence of the hummingbird trespassers which appear to enjoy being chased. After being pursued for a considerable distance, they often return close on the heels of the pursuer to hover before him as an invitation to another race.

The only serious hummingbird battles apparently occur when a new or abandoned territory is in dispute between two well-matched individuals seeking to take possession. Even then, the murderous-looking thrusts are aimed a little to one side of the adversary instead of directly at him. Hummingbird activity is most feverish during migrations when the birds are abundant, defending feeding territories, and in almost constant movement. Then pursuits are continual, but no casualties result and it seems to be all in the spirit of good fun.

The alleged pugnaciousness of the hummingbird can best be judged by observing its behavior toward other birds. While they are often seen in hot pursuit of other species, a hummingbird will not attack any other bird that refuses to enter into the game, and birds as small as goldfinches show no concern when challenged by hummingbirds. Animosity or combativeness do not seem to enter into these pursuits any more than when a small dog chases a passing vehicle. Furthermore, hummingbirds may be found nesting near other birds, apparently in complete amity; they not only show no aggressiveness, but endure the bullying of larger birds without resentment. An Anna's hummingbird, forced away from its syrup bottle by a house finch or an Audubon's warbler, has been observed to wait patiently on a nearby perch until the interloper had left.

Play is undoubtedly a dominant motive in the life of the hummingbird, especially among the immature birds. A solitary individual, hovering in the air, will rapidly spin around through one or two complete revolutions, for no conceivable reason but its own amusement. Perhaps this playfulness is the indirect result of the efficiency of the bird's mode of feeding, which leaves it with an abundance of leisure time and surplus energy at its disposal.

The energy expended in play or in defense of territories must be vastly greater than that which is necessary to the bird's maintenance. That these flights are by no means effortless may be realized on a hot day, when a hummingbird will return to a shaded perch and sit for some moments with its bill open, its whole body shaking with the violence of its panting. Despite the great amount of unnecessary flying, the difference between work and play seems to be clearly recognized, so while engaged in the prosaic business of probing the flowers, the hummingbird never misses an opportunity to take advantage of any available perch, sometimes hanging almost upside down to reach a flower without using its wings. For this reason, when hummingbirds are provided with feeding bottles of sugar water that people put up in yards to attract them, the addition of a convenient perch is greatly appreciated by them.

Hummingbirds learn through experience, thus demonstrating their mental kinship with the higher animals rather than with insects. Bright colors are in themselves attractive only to the younger individuals, which learn by trial just where their food is to be found. Once this is learned, the birds may be seen seeking out some of the smaller and more inconspicuous flowers while larger and showier ones are ignored. When installing a new hummingbird feeding station, it is much easier to attract the immature birds, whose curiosity and experimentation leads them to investigate anything unusual.

Through these feeding devices a more intimate understanding of hummingbird psychology may be obtained. Some of the birds are timid and never overcome an attitude of nervousness when visiting the feeders, while others approach them with complete assurance. The hummingbird's accurate memory for location may be demonstrated by removing a feeder that it has become accustomed to visit, after which it will return several times and hover in the air at the exact spot formerly occupied by the feeding device. On the other hand, a similar bottle of sugar water (3 parts water to 1 of sugar) in a new location will be immediately recognized and visited by them.

Perhaps because of their habitual association, hummingbirds show little fear of bees, sometimes thrusting their bills through a struggling mass of the insects at the mouth of a syrup bottle. Although bees are usually ignored, hummingbirds have been observed to dart with their bills open at flying honeybees as if threatening to bite them. Ants are treated by hummingbirds with much more respect, and a few of these walking about the mouth of a bottle of sugar water are sufficient to keep the birds away.

Experiments with perfumes, together with the seeming lack of preference for heavily scented flowers, indicate that the sense of smell is not important in the hummingbird's detection of food.

The hummingbird's hearing is well developed, and the click of a camera shutter will often cause them to fly away instantly, as does a sudden visible movement. The slight sound of the rustling dead leaves will cause hummingbirds to become alert, just as it does with many other creatures. It is probable that hummingbirds are able to distinguish all the colors of the spectrum; bits of red or blue cloth seem to attract their attention equally, while green is ignored (*See under Animal: Color Vision in Animals*).

Many naturalists believe that red flowers have a greater attraction for the birds than those of any other color; perhaps this is because red, as the complementary color, stands out most conspicuously where the prevailing background is green. In the Southwest, where backgrounds are as likely to be brown as green, hummingbirds seem to show no preference for any one color.

Notable among the hummingbird's varied activities are the courtship flights of the males, in which each species practices its own particular form or forms of flight, accompanied by sounds—some vocal, some caused by specialized flight feathers—so peculiar and characteristic in quality that any of the seven California species can usually be identified at a distance by sound alone.

In two of its qualities it does not seem that the hummingbird's equal exists anywhere in nature: first, in the luminous brilliance reflected from certain portions of the plumage; second, in its complete mastery of its movements in the air. Its instant coordination can perhaps best be realized by noting the ease with which it probes the throats of small blossoms being blown to and fro by changeable gusts of wind.

Hummingbirds are fascinating to observe, as this quote from the English artist-naturalist, John Gould suggests: "That our enthusiasm and excitement with regard to most things become lessened, if not deadened, by time, particularly when we have acquired what we vainly consider a complete knowledge of the subject, is, I fear, too often the case with most of us; not so, however, I believe, with those who take up the study of the family of hummingbirds. Certainly I can affirm that such is not the case with myself; for the pleasure which I experience on seeing a hummingbird is as great at the present moment as when I first saw one."   —R.S.W.

Recommended Reading

Hummingbirds—Crawford Greenawalt. Doubleday & Company, Inc., New York.
Hummingbirds and How To Attract Them in *Songbirds in Your Garden*—John K. Terres. Thomas Y. Crowell Company, New York.

Allen's Hummingbird
Other Common Names—Allen's hummer
Scientific Name—*Selasphorus sasin*
Family—Trochilidae (hummingbirds)
Order—Apodiformes
Size—Length, 3¼ inches
Range—Southern Oregon to Ventura County, California, in a narrow coastal strip, east to Trinity County, California. Migrates through Arizona and Baja California and winters in northwestern Mexico

The Allen's hummingbird is the California representative of the rufous hummingbird, staying to nest on the chaparral-covered slopes of the foothills and canyons of coastal California. It is so much like the rufous hummingbird that unless an observer gets a very good look at it, there seems to be little difference.

The main distinction is the center of the back, which is green. But this can be seen only at close range; at any distance the bird seems to be just as rusty as the rufous hummingbird. The females cannot be told apart in the field, even by an expert.

Anna's Hummingbird
Other Common Names—Anna's hummer
Scientific Name—*Calypte anna*
Family—Trochilidae (hummingbirds)
Order—Apodiformes
Size—Length, 4 inches
Range—Breeds in California and the northwestern part of Baja California. Resident in the lowlands west of the Sierras, north San Francisco Bay, and the head of the Sacramento Valley. In autumn it occurs farther north (to Humboldt County), and some wander southeast to southern Arizona

The Anna's hummingbird stays in California the year round, except for a few that winter in southern Arizona and northern Sonora in Mexico. The smallest gardens are visited by the Anna's and it even probes for nectar in the bright flowers in the window boxes, two or three stories above the street.

No other California hummingbird has the top of the head red; nor is any other so large. Only the male has the rose-red or purple-red crown and gorget, or brush, extending from the sides of the throat. The female looks much like the females of several other hummingbirds—green above, white below, with a double-rounded tail.

After the winter rains, often as early as January, the Anna's hummingbirds get ready to nest. The male goes through the traditional "air dance," or "pendulum dance," by which so many species of hummingbirds seek to win their mates. Back and forth he swings in an ellipse, as if he were at the end of a swinging pendulum. He dives toward his mate and zooms upward, flashing his bright colors. At the bottom of his dive, he makes a shrill sound, surprisingly loud for such a tiny mite. His demure mate watches him from her perch, head wagging from side to side, but she will appear unimpressed and fly away as if the whole performance were quite boring. He is ardent, however, and will not let her remain out of sight very long. In spite of all these attentions, he does not take the responsibility of family duties. At nesting time he seems to disappear completely, and the female must take the full burden of building the nest and raising the young.

The nest might be placed almost anywhere. Perhaps no other hummingbird shows so much originality in the choice of sites. Nests have been found on ropes, on top of electric-light bulbs, on rungs of ladders, tops of signs, and on growing fruit. Although nests and eggs have been found in December, they are most common during February and March. Occasional birds nest as late as August. The nests are always beautiful little creations, hardly an inch and a half across—tiny cradles saddled to a branch or twig, made of bits of cottony plant fibers and fluff. The two tiny white eggs are hardly larger than beans.

The bean-sized eggs hatch into two tiny, black, buglike creatures, blind and ugly. That such miserably small and helpless creatures could ever grow into birds seems almost unbelievable. In a few days the eyes open and little lines of bristlelike pinfeathers start sprouting, which give the birds a pricklylooking appearance for a while—something like tiny pincushions. When the sheathing drops off these bristles, the soft feathers make the two midgets look much more like birds. Then, for the first time, they begin to resemble the parent, which has been patiently feeding them. Their bills are much shorter, however, not quite so long and rapierlike, but as they grow older their bills lengthen.

Baby hummingbirds are fed by regurgitation, which means pumping partially digested food from the mother's crop into that of the youngster. She jabs her sharp

Anna's hummingbird (above); black-chinned hummingbird (below)

bill right down her baby's throat, while it holds on for dear life. It is like witnessing a sword-swallowing act, but the babies thrive on such rough treatment.

When the young have been in the nest nearly three weeks, they become very restless, and for two or three days they exercise their wings at the edge of the nest. Without launching themselves into the air, they buzz their wings furiously for minutes at a time. When they finally leave, they are efficient fliers. —A.B., Jr.

Black-chinned Hummingbird
Other Common Names—Black-chinned hummer
Scientific Name—*Archilochus alexandri*
Family—Trochilidae (hummingbirds)
Order—Apodiformes
Size—Length, 3¾ inches
Range—Nests from British Columbia and Montana, south through western United States to northern Baja California, east

to Arizona and Texas, South to Chihuahua, Mexico. Winters from southeastern California and northern Baja California into Mexico; accidental in Louisiana

The black-chinned hummingbird has similar habits to the closely related ruby-throated hummingbird of the Midwest and eastern United States. It builds its tiny nest on a horizontal limb, or in the fork of a tree or bush. It is often built of the down the female gathers from the undersides of the leaves of sycamore trees. She lays two white eggs.

The black-chinned hummingbird feeds freely on insects and is attracted to the sweet, gummy sap exuding from the black birch and other trees. Poising in front of these sap exudations, it snaps up insects that feed upon the sweet fluid.
—J.K.T.

Broad-tailed Hummingbird
Other Common Names—Broad-tailed hummer
Scientific Name—*Selasphorus platycercus*
Family—Trochilidae (hummingbirds)
Order—Apodiformes
Size—Length, 3¾ inches
Range—Eastern central California, northern Nevada, northern Wyoming, eastern Colorado, New Mexico, and southwestern Texas to southern Mexico and the highlands of Guatemala

The broad-tailed hummingbird is the hummingbird of the Rockies, where it is surprisingly common. Wherever one goes in the mountains, especially near streams, 'there can be heard the high trilling sound made by the wings of the males.

Like other hummingbirds, this species is an opportunist, following the blossoming of the flowers. Early in the season it first becomes noticeable around the cactus blossoms at the lower altitudes—around 4,000 feet. Later it is found rifling the gooseberry blossoms at 8,000 or 9,000 feet, and finally when the high snowfields have melted, it can be seen disporting itself amongst the profuse blooms of the high rocky slopes, up to 12,000 feet.

Of all the hummingbirds of the West, the broad-tailed hummer most resembles the ruby-throat, so familiar to easterners. One does not even need to see the broad-tailed hummingbird to identify it. The high screeching trill of the male is identification enough. The female makes scarcely any sound.

Ruby-throated Hummingbird
Other Common Names—Ruby-throat, common hummingbird
Scientific Name—*Archilochus colubris*
Family—Trochilidae (hummingbirds)
Order—Apodiformes
Size—Length, 3 to 3¾ inches
Range—Breeds from central Saskatchewan, Alberta, Manitoba, and the south shore of the Gulf of St. Lawrence, south to the Gulf of Mexico. Winters mainly in Mexico, Central America, and Panama. Some ruby-throated hummingbirds spend the winter in southern Florida, Louisiana, and Texas

Out of some 319 species of hummingbirds, the ruby-throat is the only one to visit regularly the eastern United States—with the exception of an occasional rufous hummingbird that winters on the Gulf Coast. It is a western hummingbird that nests north to Alaska.

The ruby-throated male and his white-throated mate spend the winter like true vacationists in the tropics, in Mexico, and Central America with hummingbirds of other species. When spring comes they make a nonstop flight over the trackless wastes of the Gulf of Mexico to the United States, 500 to 600 miles away. The male with his metallic blood-red gorget arrives first, early in May; his mate arrives about a week later.

Although it seems that ruby-throated hummingbirds never cease flying, they really spend as much time perching as any other birds. Dead twigs and telegraph wires make favorite perching places. There they rest, preening first one wing, then the other. The brilliant throat bib of the male, which catches the light like a burning coal, loses its glow and turns jet black with a mere turn of his head (*See under Feather: Colors of Feathers; and under Animal: Colors of Animals*).

Ruby-throated hummingbirds are very scrappy. When several of them are flying about a clump of flowers, one of the birds will sometimes attack another and try to drive it away. Back and forth they dart, parrying with their rapierlike beaks and uttering shrill, enraged, mouselike squeaks. They love combat—even a bird as large as a crow or a red-tailed hawk is not safe from annoyance when this tiny mite gets up its ire.

The ruby-throated hummingbird's pendulum dance is a courtship display with which the male seeks to win his mate. Back and forth he swings in a huge curve as if he were at the bottom of a swinging pendulum. Then, as a climax, he zooms past his future mate, flaunting his bright colors.

In spite of these earnest attentions, when nesting time comes around he disappears and leaves his mate in full charge of the home. She assumes all the responsibility and receives no help from him in the task of building the nest. It is one of the most beautiful nests of any bird. Saddled to a branch or a twig it is a walnut-sized gem of avian architecture, made of bits of cottony wool from fern stalks, bound together with spider webs and shingled with lichens. It resembles a tuft of moss or a moss-covered knot on the limb on which it rests.

Two white eggs the size of beans are laid before the nest is really completed. These are deposited about two or three days apart, therefore they do not hatch at the same time. It takes from 11 to 15 days of incubation before the tiny pink-skinned bits of life kick from the eggshells. They look more like bugs than birds at first. It would take a half-dozen of them to fill the bowl of one ordinary teaspoon.

Ruby-throated hummingbird

The rate of growth of young ruby-throated hummingbirds depends much on the amount of food brought them by the female parent. If days are fair and feeding conditions good, the young grow rapidly. A rainy period and reduced feeding by the mother bird retards their growth. At the end of 10 or 11 days the sprouting feathers, still in their sheaths, give them the appearance of pincushions or tiny porcupines—they are very prickly looking things then, not at all like the soft, well-feathered creatures of a few days later. When this horny sheathing drops off they look quite fluffy and handsome.

During all this time they are fed spiders and aphids, which their mother gleans from the curled-under tips of fresh leaves. The feeding process resembles a sword-swallowing act. The mother thrusts her thin bill deep down her youngsters' throats as if she would stab them to death. But she is quite careful—deftly placing the food in the youngster's crop without injuring the delicate throat.

The young birds usually stay in the nest about three weeks. When they leave they spring upward, helicopterlike, directly from the nest's rim. They do not need much attention after that. They quickly grasp all the facts of life: how to gather aphids from the undersurfaces of leaves, how to hang on humming wings before a blossom, and how to bathe in the dew puddles that collect on big, flat leaves.

Ruby-throated hummingbirds usually raise a second brood later in the season. But when September comes, the birds begin to migrate southward. They stop along the way to feed among the orange blossoms of the jewelweed and other tubular-shaped flowers, but do not tarry long. Flowers with nectar are difficult to find in October. Each autumn they make the return flight across the Gulf of Mexico and to their wintering grounds in Mexico and Central America. —A.B., Jr.

Rufous Hummingbird
Other Common Names—Rufous hummer
Scientific Name— *Selasphorus rufus*
Family—Trochilidae (hummingbirds)
Order—Apodiformes
Size—Length, 3½ inches
Range—Southern Alaska, western Canada, and Montana south through Washington and Oregon to northwestern California. Winters in Mexico

Of all the hundreds of hummingbirds the most adventuresome—the one that travels farthest from the tropics—is the little rufous hummingbird. This tiny thing, dressed in brilliant copper, is only 3½ inches long, and weighs no more than a penny, yet it travels all the way to the sixty-first degree of latitude on the coast of Alaska. This is even farther north than the famed ruby-throat of the East goes.

There is nothing haphazard in the wanderings of the rufous hummingbird. It seems to know just where it is going, buzzing northward through the Pacific states in the spring and south through the high mountains of the Rockies in the fall. The vanguard arrive in the lowlands of southern California early in March. Their travels seem to be one long pursuit of blossoming plants. The little travelers reach Oregon just at the time the crimson-flowered currants are in full bloom. Some stop to nest in Oregon but most of them keep on going into Washington, British Columbia, and coastal Alaska. They push northward just as fast as the spring flowers will assure them a living.

The northern summer is brief, and shortly after nesting is accomplished, they leave, but not the way they came. The valleys are dry and brown so the rufous hummingbird hordes take a route down the high mountain ranges of the interior, where lupines, pentstemons and other late summer blossoms dot the high alpine meadows. The first of these southbound birds appears early in July. On the high slopes, close against the clouds, the rufous hummingbird is sometimes unbelievably abundant in the late summer. Often a dozen will fly about one clump of flowers, squeaking angrily and chasing each other back and forth.

At birth a ruby-throated hummingbird chick barely fills the bottom of a teaspoon

A ruby-throated hummingbird hovers at the mouth of a flower

HURRICANE
Effects on Birds

When West Indian storms sweep up the Atlantic Coast and level all before them, most people tremble and others question God's wisdom. The "birdomaniac," awed by such violence but oblivious to its wantonness, scarcely thinks of the destruction of property or the loss of life; keyed up, he wonders what rare seabirds the winds will bring. Possibly nothing can keep him from hurrying to the shore—before the vortex has passed.

Most of the records of tropical seabirds in the northern United States can be traced to hurricanes. A storm in September 1876 struck the West Indies with all its fury. On many of the islands people were washed into the sea or were buried beneath their homes. Forty-five ships were battered to kindling in Puerto Rico and the American steamer *Liberty* was lost somewhere between Havana and New York. This storm, which caused so much human misery, left in its wake sooty terns in New England, a tropic bird in New York and a man-o'-war bird in Nova Scotia. All these had been picked up by the storm somewhere in the Caribbean and carried along for 2,000 miles or more before they were set down in an unfamiliar landscape.

In August 1893 a storm passed over mountainous Haiti and Dominica, wiping out fields of bananas and sugarcane, laying low the coconut palms, and scattering the boats that rode at anchor. During its passage it picked from the sea a number of black-capped petrels, a species so rare that for a while it was thought to be extinct, and dropped them exhausted or dying in Virginia, New York, Massachusetts, and Vermont. Five years later, after an October hurricane that swept inland to the Mississippi, two more of these petrels, which look somewhat like greater shearwaters, were captured in Kentucky and Ohio.

Storm-blown Sooty Terns

The sooty tern, the "sea swallow" with the black back and white breast, seems to be the most frequent of these oceanic waifs (*See Tern*). The native people of some of the Lesser Antilles call them "hurricane birds" because great numbers of them often appear out of a seemingly birdless sea just before a blow. Ober tells of this in his *Camps in the Caribbees*, written in 1880:

"Immediately preceding the hurricanes there arrive off the Caribbean coast (of Dominica) vast numbers of birds called from their cries Twa-oo. They are said to be the harbingers of hurricanes and they appear only during the calms immediately before a storm. They cover the water in large flocks and come in from the desolate sandy beaches where they breed. They are the sooty tern ... When I arrived in Dominica the sea was black with them, but on the morning after the storm they had disappeared to a bird, as completely as though blown into another sphere."

In the third week of September in 1933 the north Atlantic shores were peppered with sooties just after a wild storm had ravaged the coast. Two days later a beautiful specimen was found lying dead among the drift on the marsh grass on Staten Island, New York. The nearest place of origin of this bird would be the Bahamas or the Dry Tortugas off Key West. The following January, an observer, searching for winter seabirds along the bluffs at Montauk Point on the eastern tip of Long Island, spied a bleached skeleton, half buried in the sand. Pulling it out, he saw by its long black bill it belonged to a sooty tern, undoubtedly another casualty of this same storm.

Hurricane's Effects Near Cape Canaveral

During September 1945 when an ornithologist was stationed at the air base at Orlando, Florida, the storm warnings went up. All planes were sent scurrying to safer airfields to the north. For hours the driving drizzle sounded on the roof while the howling wind slowly increased

The 180-miles-per-hour winds of Hurricane Donna lashed Florida Bay, Everglades National Park, on September 10, 1960 (above). Ten thousand herons, egrets, spoonbills, and ibises were killed, many in tangled debris such as that shown (below)

its tempo. When the storm reached the peak of its fury, limbs of pine trees, roofing paper, shingles and boards hurtled through the air, but the buildings held fast. The following day the ornithologist drove to Cape Canaveral on the east coast and there, on the lighthouse keeper's well-kept lawn, he picked up two dead birds. One was a sooty tern and the other, slightly smaller and paler, with a light nape was a bridled tern, the fifth record for Florida. The keeper of the light said that there had been several others on the lawn in the morning before the cats got them. During the night, he reported, when the gales were still raging, clouds of sooties, or wide-awakes, fluttered before the huge lenses. It must have been an eery sight. Once the storm is spent the birds seem to disappear into the void, as if they were the souls of lost sailors; and though one might stand on the dunes and search he would not see a sooty or a noddy.

Origin of Atlantic Hurricanes

According to the dictionary, the word *hurricane* comes from *hurakan* of the Taino Indians of the West Indies. It is used by mariners to denote a wind force of more than 75 miler per hour, which Admiral Francis Beaufort described as "that which no canvas could withstand."

The majority of hurricanes in the Atlantic originate in late August, September, or early October, between 10 and 20 degrees north of the equator, out toward the Cape Verdes, far to the east of the Caribbean. As if the gods conspired to stir the oppressively hot and humid doldrums into action, winds and squalls start converging on the overheated patch of ocean until a revolving tropical storm is born. Moving westward and gaining force, it skirts that fabulous waste of drifting seaweed, the Sargasso Sea, which is an anticyclone (high pressure) area. To avoid this region of opposing air currents the cyclonic storms must pass through the West Indies before

swinging violently northward and then northeastward to final dissipation. Anywhere from two hurricanes to a dozen or more are reported each year. Not all of them reach the United States; but when they do, they usually skirt the coast. A few pass inland before turning out to sea.

The system of one of these storms is like a whirlpool, sucking the winds into its vortex in a counterclockwise direction. These winds come from a long distance and attain a speed sometimes exceeding 100 miles per hour. On the

Blue-faced boobies live in the hurricane belt and are only accidentally blown to the shores of northern North America

bosom of these violent gales, which pour into the storm center from all points of the compass, birds are borne like swimmers in a strong current. It is not unusual then, after a hurricane, to find birds not only of southern origin, but also from the Northeast or the West. After one such September storm had passed over Long Island many scores of skimmers and Forster's terns from the South were seen on the same mud flat; also seen were golden plovers that normally bypass Long Island to the east, out at sea; and, most remarkable of all, an avocet from the West.

The "Eye" of the Storm

At the center of a cyclonic storm is a dead spot, from 5 to 25 miles across, where the winds are lulled. This calm area, or "eye" travels along at a relatively slow pace at first, perhaps not more than 15 miles per hour, but as it moves northward it gains speed, traveling as much as 30 miles per hour or more. As the whirlpool grows wider, it loses its destructive potency.

Robert Cushman Murphy, the famous student of oceanic birdlife believes that many birds actually travel within this "eye." Once caught *inside* the swirl of the storm, he says, "they might be carried along without becoming panicky, without experiencing any sense of difficulty, feeding normally and tending always to turn inward toward the calm of the slow-moving center when they had flown far enough in one direction to come into heavily wind-whipped waters. Only when the vortex comes into close proximity with the land, as I conceive the situation, would birds thus held in unconscious durance begin to fight the gales, perhaps to be carried into the higher altitudes of the atmosphere and to be buffeted as helpless waifs for long distances overland before being cast out centrifugally, subsequently to fall exhausted. It is only through some such process as this that I can comprehend the transportation of black-capped petrels from points east of the Caribbean to the Mississippi Valley, or of Madeira and South Trinidad petrels from the central or eastern north equatorial Atlantic to Ottawa and Ithaca, respectively."

There are actual records of the presence of birds in the center of hurricanes. Ships entering the windless eye have found the air filled with the fluttering wings of seafowl, and the decks and rigging were sought as resting places by hundreds of small landbirds.

Great Hurricane of 1938

One of the most destructive hurricanes on record (in the United States, at least) struck New England on September 21, 1938. It started as any other ordinary hurricane, but before it reached Florida where everyone awaited it, tense and expectant, it veered and raced to the north. Instead of growing weaker as it went along, its winds became more violent. The storm was hemmed in by two high pressure areas, one to the west on land and another to the east at sea. Between lay a passageway across New England, a low pressure corridor of light air. Forced into this path of least resistance, the hurricane hit the eastern end of Long Island with a huge wave that swept great stone mansions off the dunes. Water rose 15 or 20 feet and many people drifted for hours on rafts that had been the roofs of their homes.

Spinning overland, it tore across Long Island, sending the century-old elms in East Hampton and Bridgehampton crashing across the highways. Seven hundred summer homes at Watch Hill, Rhode Island, were washed away. In Providence the crest of the tidal wave swept into the downtown business section and drowned a man in front of the City Hall. Fantastic as it sounds, passengers were reported drowned in a train stalled on the tracks between Boston and New York.

The sea storm became a land storm, a sort of supercyclone. Church steeples were snapped off in little towns in the

Connecticut Valley, and forests of white pine were laid down like matchsticks on New England hillsides. Even the anemometers, by which men measure the wind, blew away, but the one on Mount Washington held fast. It recorded a velocity of 183 miles per hour. On the next day, the 22nd of September, the equatorial storm roared into Canada, weakened, and slowly passed away.

Although there had been very little official warning, there was no doubt, as it approached, that this was not an ordinary storm. The barometer at the offices of the National Audubon Society in New York went into a nose dive. When word came of the storm out on Long Island, the first thought of the ornithologists of Audubon House was about the birds out on the island.

If rare birds had been brought by lesser storms, what would this one bring? One birdwatcher came by the Audubon office to report that he had gone out on the marshes at sunset, when the gales from the south were still blowing strong into the retreating storm center. Clapper rails, flooded out of the salt meadows, were crushed by cars on the highway. On a mud flat he had seen several suspicious looking terns. From his description they appeared to be sooties.

Ornithologist and amateur birdwatchers alike cruised beach after beach within 30 miles of New York, but saw even fewer birds than usual. Only a few gulls were around, and the small shorebirds were completely dispersed by the storm. A small dark seabird that scaled by beyond the surf was seen, but it was lost among the waves before it could be identified. The brief glimpse suggested an Audubon's shearwater, a resident of the Bahamas. Aside from that one unsatisfactory observation there was nothing exciting. Where were the fancy birds that should have been seen? Other members of the Linnaean Society, the bird club of Manhattan, scoured Long Island and asked the same question.

Effects on Birds

Not until a week or two later was the answer known. Yellow-billed tropic birds that nest in the coral caves of the Bermudas, were borne across Long Island, up the Connecticut Valley, through western Massachusetts and were dropped like spent meteors at three places in Vermont. How many of these streamlined wanderers came to earth but were never found, no one will know.

Cory's shearwaters and greater shearwaters, gull-like travelers of the ocean spaces, which never of their own volition leave salt water, were found inland in Massachusetts and in Vermont, hundreds of miles from their element. Leach's petrels, the dark swallowlike storm petrel with the white rump patch and the notched tail, were scattered through the heart of New England. Its small square-tailed cousin, the Wilson's petrel, the one that follows boats at sea, was recorded on Lake Ontario, Lake Champlain, and on the St. Lawrence River.

If Robert Cushman Murphy's explanation is accepted, the birds had followed the tranquil eye of the storm until it reached Long Island. As land approached, they struggled offshore to keep over the water, the element over which they were most at home. Encountering the revolving winds again, they fought to leeward until they were carried up and up into the mad swirl. Once trapped there was no escape until they were thrown out, exhausted or dying, hundreds of miles from their familiar environment.

What do these storms do to the lives of birds? Some of the seabirds die, particularly when the hurricane travels overland. But in most storms that dissipate themselves over the ocean, the birds ride out the tempest then return to home waters posthaste. No birds have a keener homing ability than the pelagic birds; the unleashed winds are a routine part of their lives.

But the myriads of small migrating landbirds that are trapped within the

Natives in the Lesser Antilles call the sooty tern "hurricane bird," because it often appears in great numbers just before a blow

windless eye probably never see land again if the storm dies far out over the Atlantic. One wonders what the effect would be on the few Kirtland's warblers that nest in the northern United States if they were intercepted by an October hurricane while making the flight to their winter home in the Bahamas.

It is known that the dwindling population of the great white heron was cut way down by the Labor Day hurricane of 1935. During this storm, which took so many lives, 15 feet of water swept across the Matecumbe Keys of southern Florida. A month after the storm, when Alexander Sprunt, Jr. flew over nine-tenths of the range of this largest of all American herons, he saw only 146 birds, and in the center of the swath cut by the wind and waves, where everything looked as though flattened by a steam roller, not a bird could be found.

Small Birds in a Hurricane

Another ornithologist, George M. Sutton, had the presence of mind, during a violent October hurricane in Florida, to watch the small birds in order to see how they fared. The battering winds reached 78 miles per hour, with gusts up to 108 miles per hour. The blue jays seemed to enjoy it all, but a mockingbird squatted behind one of the solid supports of a low porch. A shrike, dispossessed from a clump of Spanish moss in an oak tree when the trunk snapped, scrambled to the lee of an outhouse. Palm warblers hid under porches, under ventilators, and among the grasses. A flicker hurtled out of a falling pine, bounced on the ground, and dazedly flew to the trunk of a sturdier tree. All the birds seemed to survive, for in the afternoon, with the storm's passing, the cardinals, ground doves, red-bellied woodpeckers, and others came forth from their hiding places unharmed.

The real effect of a hurricane on landbirds is an indirect one, one that might not be felt until the following year or even several years later. When the hurricane of October 17-18, 1944 blasted the west coast of Florida, it blew down 18 trees where eagles nested, threw many nests to the ground, and damaged all the others (*See under Eagle: The Bald Eagle*). Although the birds rebuilt all but 1, they laid no eggs that season in 24 of them. In 21 others the eggs did not hatch, for some unknown reason. Thus 45 nests out of 115 were failures in 1945, because of that one storm, which set up a chain of reactions that upset the Florida bald eagle's pattern of life.

Beneficial Effects of a Hurricane

It would be trite to moralize about "an ill wind," but the great New England hurricane of 1938, which brought death to so many seabirds, made survival easier for some of the small birds that nested on land in the northeastern United States, as the next several years proved. The ravaged woodlands were opened up; there were more clearings on New England mountainsides for olivesided flycatchers and white-throated sparrows; more piles of brush for winter wrens to hide in; more decaying timber for woodpeckers to forage in. Wendell Smith, Vermont's most outstanding amateur ornithologist, had made a breeding census of a 50-acre tract of pine-hemlock forest near his home. In 1936 he found 75 pairs of birds representing 32 species. That was before the great storm tore through and littered the ground with the fallen conifers. The summer after the blowdown there were not fewer birds but more, and each year for 9 years the number kept climbing until in 1947 there

were 187 pairs of birds, representing 46 species—an increase in density of 150 percent.   —R.T.P.

Hurricane Donna

In one long night and morning, September 9-10, 1960, Hurricane Donna dealt lower Florida a savage battering.

With peak winds of at least 180 miles per hour, accompanied by a rise of water that reached as much as 13 feet above normal low tide, Donna was a storm to remember. Not since the Labor Day hurricane of 1935, 25 years before almost to the day, had a storm of comparable destructiveness visited southern Florida.

A year later, towns that had been ravaged as any wartime beachhead had been rebuilt, and little remained of Donna's greatly publicized damage to the works of man. Only later was it possible to give a rounded estimate of the equally impressive—but little reported—effects upon wildlife.

Of chief concern to ornithologists and conservationists was Donna's impact upon bird populations in the area from the middle Florida Keys across Florida Bay and Cape Sable to the southwest coast. Observations centered around Flamingo, formerly a small fishing village that has become the hub of visitor activities in Everglades National Park. This is about midway in the area where Donna attained greatest intensity.

The hurricane log of District Ranger Ernest J. Borgman, National Park Service, who remained at Flamingo, reveals characteristics of the storm that helped determine its effects upon birdlife.

The morning of September 9 at Flamingo was overcast with some rain. By late afternoon the wind had not risen above about 30 miles per hour. There was little sign of the impending storm and nothing to indicate that birds in any way sensed its imminence or had attempted to move out of its path. Apparently they went to roost as on any other rainy, evening without instinctive anticipation of what was to come.

The highest winds, of undetermined velocity because the anemometer and the roof supporting it had blown away earlier, occurred about 2 to 6 a.m. on September 10. By midnight the steady push of the wind from the northeast had reduced much of Florida Bay to a bare mudflat.

As the storm passed, the wind shifted to east and southeast, reaching due south about 5:30 a.m. Then, abruptly in the early morning darkness, the water came back as a 12-foot storm wave. Something of the extent of the deluge may be judged from the fact that a number of large sea turtles and at least one porpoise rode the wave far inland and were left landlocked when it receded.

Destruction of Plantlife and Birds

The scene at Flamingo, immediately after Donna, was so changed that it was difficult to comprehend. Forests were shattered; most trees that still stood had lost all but the larger branches. Except for a few tattered palm tops no green met the eye. The landscape was brown, as if brushed by fire.

Flotsam of endless variety was deposited from the shore a mile or more inland: mud, dead fish and other marine animals, twigs, branches, uprooted trees, and every sort of human artifact from boats to bathtubs. Great hayricks of turtle grass and other plants torn from the bottom of Florida Bay marked the limit of the storm wave's advance.

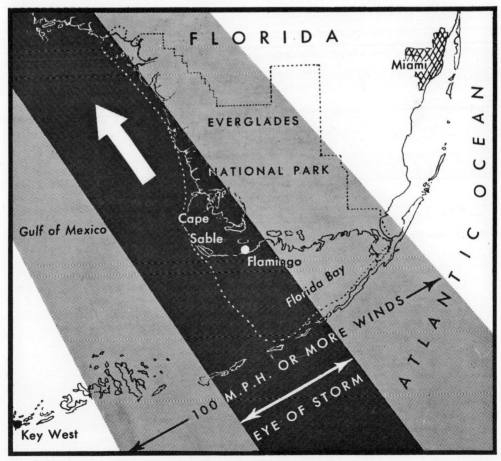

The path of Hurricane Donna

Along the lines of drift, and hanging haphazardly from denuded trees were a few dead birds: brown pelicans, common egrets, herons, and white ibises.

Air patrols soon determined that a belt of similar damage extended across western Florida Bay and north along the Gulf Coast to Everglades City. From the air it could also be seen that in some places birds had suffered much heavier mortality than was obvious in the immediate area of Flamingo.

With these observations an effort was begun to evaluate the direct and delayed effects of Donna upon the birdlife of the devastated region.

As soon as boats were available, a systematic search for dead birds was begun. Careful coverage of the tangled debris proved to be slow, difficult work. By May 1961 searches of 15 of the low islands in Florida Bay, several miles of shore at Snake Bight east of Flamingo, the west end of Bear Lake, and scattered other localities had yielded 621 dead birds of 20 species.

The list of known avian storm casualties included: 213 white ibises (204 adults, only 9 immature birds), 135 common egrets, 72 great white herons, 33 great blue herons, 21 little blue herons, 19 brown pelicans, 18 snowy egrets, 10 double-crested cormorants, 6 roseate spoonbills, 5 turkey vultures, 4 Louisiana herons, 4 yellow-crowned night herons, 2 brown noddies, one each of the black-crowned night heron, red-shouldered hawk, bald eagle, osprey, laughing gull, sooty tern, and common grackle, plus a collection of skeletons of 72 small herons, mostly little blues and snowy egrets.

Except for the two terns, all were common resident birds of Florida. The noddies and the sooty tern undoubtedly were hurricane waifs. Both of these pelagic species, and the bridled tern as well, had been seen in numbers along the southeast coast of Florida immediately before, and for several days after, the storm.

Birds Killed on Roosts

From the distribution of the dead birds it seemed clear that most were killed at roost and that they were killed by the storm wave, not swept away by the winds. Large numbers were found only at known roosts and at places where waterborne drift from roosts was deposited.

At some of these sites the concentrated mortality was appalling. On three tiny islands in the west end of Bear Lake were the remains of 140 common egrets, small herons, and white ibises.

As the dead birds were counted, survivors streamed to roost in the same battered and leafless mangrove clumps. An area of about 200 by 50 yards at Snake Bight, where drift from the large roost on Catfish Key came to rest, yielded 187 individuals of 9 species.

No close estimate of total mortality is possible. The scarcity of many shore-

Casualty of Hurricane Donna, a common egret hangs limply in the branches of a tree

birds, gulls and terns, as well as land-birds around Flamingo after the storm suggested heavy losses, but little direct evidence appeared. Smaller birds must have been battered beyond recognition or buried in the debris.

Even among the wading birds it was obvious that the larger and heavier species more often were found in the roosting areas, whereas smaller species commonly were swept away from roosts and scattered along the course of the storm wave. The number of great white herons found dead, for example, was undoubtedly much nearer actual mortality in the areas searched than was the number of white ibises.

Six hundred wading birds were discovered in searches that covered fewer than one-third of the places where appreciable numbers of dead birds were seen from the air. A more complete estimate would be that at least 10,000 herons, egrets, ibises, and roseate spoonbills were killed in Everglades National Park by Hurricane Donna (*See also under Hail and under Longspur*).

In addition to the search for dead birds, a project was undertaken to learn as much as possible about the survival and subsequent nesting success of several rare or locally distributed species. One of these, the great white heron, was almost exterminated by an earlier storm, the Labor Day hurricane of 1935. In a survey conducted for the National Audubon Society, Alexander Sprunt, Jr. could find no more than 150 great white herons after that storm. The hurricane toll of 1935 was exacted from a population already much depleted by illegal hunting.

The Great White Heron

The recovery of the great white heron is an outstanding success story of conservation work in southern Florida. With strict protection the population of great whites had increased to at least 1,500 by the late 1950's. In July 1960, six weeks before Donna, 898 were counted in Florida Bay alone. The aerial census

was repeated in late September and 546 were found.

The apparent toll of great white herons taken by Donna, about 350, was more than twice the entire population of 25 years before, yet the great whites' survival was not threatened. Survivors in Florida Bay resumed nesting almost at once. Within 10 days after the storm the birds were seen standing on new nest platforms and by May 1961 the species had substantially recovered its losses.

Effects on Rare Species

Despite many years of protection reddish egrets still are rare in Florida, perhaps numbering no more than 200 (*See under Egret*). Counts before and after Donna, however, indicated little storm loss. The population center of the species (eastern and central Florida Bay) escaped the worst effects of the storm wave that was so destructive in areas farther west.

Few wood storks and few adult roseate spoonbills encountered Donna because most of them leave southern Florida in summer. Both species returned in normal season and enjoyed generally successful nesting, despite severe storm damage to vegetation at some of the rookeries.

It was of particular interest to know how bald eagles had fared because of concern for the future of this species. The coastal mangrove wilderness in and near Everglades National Park is one of the few remaining areas in eastern North America where numbers of eaglets still are fledged each year.

Eagles were preparing to nest when Donna struck, a situation recalling the late Charles Broley's account of a much less severe Florida hurricane that was followed by a disastrously poor breeding season (*See under Eagle: Bald Eagle*).

The first survey after Donna was not encouraging. Of 41 eyries in good repair in July 1960 only 5 remained. At many places the eagle trees were gone and the forest so scrambled that no one could be certain where the trees had

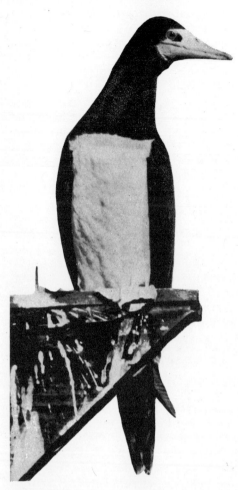

The brown booby is a West Indian bird that has been carried to Long Island, New York, and Cape Cod, Massachusetts, by hurricanes

stood. As the season progressed, some pairs of eagles were observed rebuilding nests, but doubt remained about whether they would nest after the storm. Many of the eagles studied by Broley also had rebuilt but failed to rear young in the winter following the storm. Then, in early January 1961 Park Service Ranger-Pilot Ralph Miele reported young eagles in several of the new nests.

Ultimately, new nests were built by eagles near 26 of 36 former sites. Of the remaining 10 pairs, 3 stayed near former sites without rebuilding, some may have rebuilt at a distance, and a few doubtless were killed by the storm. The final tally for bald eagle breeding season "Donna plus one" showed at least 29 young bald eagles fledged in the area covered by the park's air patrol.

Total production was slightly above that of the year before. The percentage of successful nests and the number of young per successful nest were only slightly below results for 1960.

Although few dead landbirds were found, the results of Christmas Bird Counts in the storm area confirmed earlier impressions that many species were much scarcer after Donna. On the Coot Bay Count, which includes Flamingo, most resident landbirds had decreased 50 percent or more from the numbers of the previous year.

The 1961 count of eastern meadowlarks, for example, was 16 as against an average of 119 for the 4 preceding counts. Heaviest mortality apparently occurred in places that took the full force of the storm wave.

Analysis of party lists from the Coot Bay Count showed that resident landbirds were four times more numerous one to two miles inland than they were in a similar habitat within one-half mile of the coast.

A year of close observation along Donna's trail greatly reinforced man's initial respect for the power of a major hurricane. These occasional tropical storms of extreme intensity completely dominate the natural scene along low coasts in southern Florida.

Even more impressive, however, is the ability of bird populations to survive severe hurricanes. Despite heavy mortality, no bird species was completely lost from the area as a result of Donna. Most species appear likely to regain former abundance within a few years following a severe tropical storm.

—W.B.R. Jr. and H.B.M.

HYDROCYCLE (*See under Sun*)

I

IBIS

Long-legged wading birds, at home in freshwater swamps or mud flats along the coast, the ibises are members of a tropical and warm temperate zone family. The family includes the spoonbills, which have a spatulate tip to the bill, and the ibises.

The food of ibises is largely aquatic in origin, consisting of crayfishes, worms, and insect larvae. The bills of most ibises are used to probe deeply in the mud for these animals. Spoonbills sift out their food. Upon occasion, the birds will come out of the water to march through fields of newly cut grass, eating grasshoppers and other insects.

All of the ibises have patches of bare skin extending from the bill to the back of the eye. This characteristic is carried to extremes in certain African species, such as the sacred ibis, that have no feathers on the head and neck.

The white ibis, the glossy ibis, and the white-faced ibis, occur naturally in the United States. The scarlet ibis, a South American species, was recently introduced in a park north of Miami, Florida, where it now appears to be breeding naturally.   —G.B.S.

Glossy Ibis
Other Common Names — Green ibis, liver, black curlew
Scientific Name — *Plegadis falcinellus*
Family — Threskiornithidae (ibises and spoonbills)

Order — Ciconiiformes
Size — Length, 22 inches
Range — Nests from southern Texas, east to Florida, north to South Carolina, Maryland, New Jersey, and Long Island, southward from Florida to parts of the West Indies. In Old World from southern Russia, Spain, Italy, Austria, Rumania, Iran, Turkestan, Afghanistan, southeastern Asia, Australia, Africa, Ceylon, and Philippines

The principal natural haunts of this handsome ibis in North America are the large freshwater marshes and inland lakes of Florida. It is a very dark bird, and whether at rest or in flight it is easy to see why the local name of black curlew is applied. It is not black, however, but bronze-green and chestnut, with purplish reflections. The rather slender build, down-curved beak, and general contour, strongly suggest a curlew, this term being given to both the glossy ibis and the white ibis.

Much of our knowledge of the behavior of the glossy ibis at the nest, incubation, care of the young, and other details has been furnished by a veteran birdman of Florida, Oscar E. Baynard. He found that the adults are much devoted to each other and maintain this attitude until the young are ready to fly. The female does most of the incubating and the eggs take exactly three weeks to hatch.

Cutworms, grasshoppers, crayfishes, and snakes make up its diet. Of snakes brought by the adults to one set of nestlings, there were 147 — 95 percent of which were young moccasins. (Although the species is not mentioned, it goes almost without saying that the common cottonmouth moccasin of Florida waterways is referred to.) The food is regurgitated at the nest by the adults, and the young procure it by thrusting their beaks into the parents' throats. When the young are stronger, the food is ejected into the nest by the adults and picked up by the youngsters. Feeding always takes place in the nest and not on adjacent perches.

The eggs of this species, as well as those of the white-faced ibis, are unlike those of either the white or scarlet ibises, being unmarked and of a deep greenish-blue, much like those of herons.

Scarlet Ibis

Other Common Names—Red ibis, red curlew
Scientific Name— *Eudocimus ruber*
Family—Threskiornithidae (ibises and spoonbills)
Order—Ciconiiformes
Size—Length, 22 inches
Range—Northern South America from northwestern Venezuela, Trinidad, the Guianas, and coastal Brazil; introduced into Florida and now successfully breeding

The scarlet ibis was long thought by many ornithologists to be a colored variety of the white ibis, *Eudocimus albus*, since except for color, they are identical in size and form. Recent observations at a breeding colony on the Orinoco River in Venezuela, where more than 10,000 of these birds breed, revealed that 5 percent of the birds were white. In the only case of a nesting white ibis located, it was established that the mate was also white. This record was of much interest to ornithologists since it suggests that the scarlet ibis and the white ibis may really be of the same species.

White Ibis

Other Common Names—Spanish curlew, stone curlew
Scientific Name— *Eudocimus albus*
Family—Threskiornithidae (ibises and spoonbills)
Order—Ciconiiformes
Size—Length, 25 inches
Range—A resident bird from the Gulf Coast, southeastern Georgia, and South Carolina, south from Florida to the West Indies and along Mexican coast to northern Venezuela. From Baja California south to Sinaloa east to coastal Texas, and southern Louisiana

The activities and movements of the herons, egrets, and ibises in regard to nesting sites, feeding grounds, and roosting localities are, as yet, imperfectly understood. Water levels and conditions of food supply affect the availability of both breeding and roosting areas and these may, and do, change from season to season and even in shorter cycles. The reason is sometimes obvious and sometimes obscure. This is more apparent, perhaps, in Florida than anywhere else, since parts of Florida constitute the heart of the white ibis country. The species is fairly common in Texas and parts of the Gulf Coast, but in South Carolina and Georgia there are only scattered colonies of no great size. It is Florida that one thinks of first in connection with the white ibis.

The nesting concentrations of the species are astonishing illustrations of avian community life. Not even the populous gatherings of terns and skimmers on some of the southern sandy beaches exceed the dense congregations of the white ibis in the mangrove swamps or freshwater marshes of Florida. Usually a chosen area is returned to year after year, depending, of course, on changes in the food supply and the availability of nesting sites. Just as too much water may mean the desertion of an area used for some years, so may too little. A dropping off of the crayfish population—a principal food—through one cause or another may constitute a factor (*See Crayfish*). Shooting, of course, will ruin any rookery, and so will many other human activities. Too many visitors, no matter how sympathetic and interested they may be, will result in a serious menace. The airplane has become a hazard and when piloted by a thoughtless or heedless operator can and has made birds desert a rookery en masse.

The National Audubon Society guards

Glossy ibises (above); white-faced ibis (below)

areas in Florida to which the white ibis regularly returns, both as a nesting and roosting species (*See Corkscrew Swamp; and Wood Stork*). The habit of community roosting is almost as marked as the breeding concentrations, and the protection of the roosts is highly important. Although nowhere considered a gamebird, the ibis is still shot for food by many local people. Therefore, in any known gathering place they are liable to persecution, and constant care must be undertaken to keep such areas inviolate. Some native Floridians in remote areas resent this curtailment of what they consider a natural right, for they have always followed the custom of living off the country and intend to continue the practice as long as they can (*See also under Hurricane: Effects on Birds*).

Persecution of the species is not confined to native persecution, however. Winter tourists cruise down the coast, encounter a flyway or roost of the birds and proceed to use them as living targets. No use is made of the dead whatever; they are allowed to lie where they fall, and the thoughtless killers proceed on their way, no doubt pleased with their marksmanship.

The National Audubon Society wardens patrolling the lower west coast of Florida have a vast territory to cover; unable to be in more than one place at a time, they can cope with only some of these difficulties. However, the persistence of the white ibis as a nesting bird speaks eloquently of their efforts, and protection has surely proved its worth throughout the years.

The largest rookery anywhere in the United States is at the Alafia Bank Audubon Sanctuary near Tampa, Florida.

Late in the afternoon the birds that have been out feeding return to their rookeries in long files of varying numbers. Sometimes many miles intervene between nests and food supply, and to sit under a flight line and watch the birds come in is a memorable experience. They pass almost continuously, for hours, sometimes well after dark. A reverse flight takes place in early morning, and during the day there is always some to-and-fro movement as individuals come and go between the rookery and distant feeding grounds.

The persistence of the white ibis is a gratifying thing to contemplate in this day of disappearing wildlife. Although diminished in numbers, the remnants stand as a vivid proof of what can be accomplished by determined protection of both the nesting rookeries and the feeding grounds.

White-faced Ibis
Other Common Names — White-faced glossy ibis
Scientific Name — *Plegadis chihi*
Family — Threskiornithidae (ibises and spoonbills)
Order — Ciconiiformes
Size — Length, 23 inches
Range — Breeds in California, Oregon, Utah, Colorado, Nebraska, and Minnesota south, locally, to Gulf Coast Mexico, Central and South America

The white-faced ibis is the western counterpart of the glossy ibis, differing largely in the feature that gives the species its name. It is, however, far more numerous and exhibits other differences in nesting and distribution. Several areas to which this species resorts regularly to nest are of many years' standing. Malheur Lake, Oregon, the Bear River marshes in Utah, San Jacinto Lake, California, Washoe Lake, Nevada, and various parts of Texas are examples. It is natural to suppose that the white face would constitute a good field mark, but it is not always easy to see, so that field identification is sometimes difficult. The glossy ibis has a narrow bluish rim of bare skin in front of the eye. In photographs this appears to be white, and pictures, other than in color, are therefore misleading. The white band on the face of the white-faced ibis extends to the throat and side of head just back of the eye. Also, this bird has

*A white **ibis** stands watchfully in its nest built in a low tree*

a dull reddish cast to the bill and legs. This reddish cast is not conspicuous, however, being merely a suffusion, whereas the basic color is dark brown or black.

The white-faced ibis breeds commonly in parts of Texas, especially in the eastern portions of the state, between Port Lavaca and Corpus Christi. They once nested in some abundance near Brownsville, and some few no doubt still do so; but drainage and irrigation projects have greatly diminished suitable marsh habitats.

Like the glossy ibis, this species is a lover of fresh water, using sloughs, lakes, and marshes as nesting sites. However, it sometimes resorts to the coast and may be found breeding in tidal waters.

Even though the species is not a gamebird, some are killed by the native population in nearly all parts of the range. The majority of the heron-egret-ibis tribe, however, are well regarded in Texas, because they devour the crayfishes that burrow into the rice field banks and cause losses to agriculture.

ICE (*See under Frost*)

IGUANA (*See under Reptile*)

The lacewing fly lays its eggs on slender stalks among aphid colonies

INSECT
The Place of Insects in the Animal Kingdom

Insects constitute the class Insecta or Hexapoda (both names are correct) of the phylum Arthropoda, the great group of invertebrate animals characterized by the possession of an external skeleton and jointed legs. The jointed legs distinguish arthropods from members of the phylum Annelida — earthworms, leeches, and marine worms — which also have external skeletons. If an annelid has legs at all, they are bristles or unjointed fleshy lobes projecting from the sides of the body. Arthropods and annelids together make up the superphylum Annulata — the *ringed animals* — so called because the body is organized into a series of similar segments rather like a string of cylindrical heads. Externally, the stiff or leathery skin that is the skeleton of the animal is divided into rings with narrow bands of softer and more elastic skin between them to permit movement. Internally, most of the organs must once have been repeated in each segment, though the arrangement has been somewhat modified in modern annulates.

The first arthropod was probably a wormlike creature with one pair of jointed legs on every segment of its long body except the first and last (See *Arthropod*). On the first segment was a pair of antennae or feelers and a pair of eyes. The mouth was on the bottom in the joint between the first and second segments. The rearmost segment was a simple cap with the anus in the middle of it. It is likely that the legs were biramous, or two-branched, like those of many living aquatic arthropods, the inner branch being a feathery gill. This common ancestor of all arthropods lived in the sea, so long ago that no record of its appearance has been preserved. We know what it must have been like by comparative study of present-day species in all stages of development and of such fossils as have been discovered.

In all known arthropods, whether living or fossil, groups of segments have become consolidated into regions with specialized functions, and the legs of some segments have been lost or made over for uses other than walking and breathing. Arthropods are classified according to the degree of this consolidation and the number and uses of the remaining appendages.

The formation of a head from several segments and the adaptation of the legs of some of these segments into feeding tools may well have been the earliest specialization. Long before any of the arthropods became land animals the phylum had split into two branches distinguishable by the form of their mouthparts.

In the subphylum Chelicerata there is one pair of "jaws" called chelicerae which are tipped with pinchers for crushing food. These move forward and backward in a line roughly parallel with the long axis of the body. There is also a pair of feelers called pedipalps, still very leglike, covered with tiny sense organs for locating food by touch, taste, and smell. The antennae of the primitive arthropod have been lost. Spiders, scorpions, ticks, and their many cousins of the class Arachnida are chelicerates. So are these living fossils the horseshoe crabs (see *Horseshoe Crab*), class Xiphosurida, and the giant extinct sea scorpions, class Eurypterida. Probably the sea spiders, class Pycnogonida, are chelicerates too, but it is hard to tell because they have lost their mouthparts altogether.

Members of the subphylum Mandibulata have at least two and usually three or more pairs of "jaws." These move in and out in a line roughly at right angles to the long axis of the body. The foremost pair are called mandibles. They are hard, sharp-edged, and often toothed, and work like a pair of shears. The other mouthparts, called maxillae, are more fleshy and covered with hairs and spines. They work like fingers to manipulate the food. Each maxilla has a palpus or feeler of its own; there are no pedipalps. The primitive antennae have been retained. A second pair of antennae derived from a pair of primitive legs was once common, but it has been lost in all modern mandibulates except the crustacea, a huge class of predominently aquatic arthropods which includes crabs, lobsters, shrimp, and the familiar terrestrial pill bugs or wood lice (*See Crustacean*). Centipedes or hundred-leggers, the class Chilopoda, and millipedes or thousand-leggers, the class Diplopoda, are also mandibulates, as are several other classes small both in number of species and size of animal. Insects too are mandibulates, and by very far the largest class not only of arthropods but of the entire Animal Kingdom. Their species outnumber those of all other groups of animals put together by roughly four to one.

Insects are distinguished from other mandibulates by a combination of quite conspicuous characteristics. The body is organized into three sections, the head, the thorax, and the abdomen. There are one pair of antennae, a pair of compound eyes (each made up of many units capable of independent vision), and three simple eyes. There are three pairs of mouthparts, three pairs of legs, and usually two pairs of wings. These characteristics apply to adult insects and to the young of those kinds which do not change form greatly during growth. Many young insects show hardly any of the characteristic features. There are also exceptions to all the rules among adult insects, but seldom so many exceptions in any one species that confusion is possible. (For example, in some butterflies the front feet are reduced to mere stubs hidden in the "fur" of the body so that the animal appears to be four-footed, but nobody could mistake such a butterfly for anything other than an insect.) Other arthropods may resemble insects in one or more of the key characteristics, but seldom in enough

of them to cause uncertainty. (For example, a baby tick has six legs, not eight like the adult; but its body is consolidated into a single piece, not three, and it has no antennae and no compound eyes.)

Of the two scientific names used for insects in general, Insecta means *cutinto* or *sliced animals*, a reference to the segmented structure common to all annulates. Hexapoda means *six-footed animals*. Since counting the legs is the easiest way to tell insects from distant relatives like spiders (eight legs) Hexapoda seems to be the more useful name.

The Anatomy and Physiology of Insects

Insects are animals, and like other animals they must take in food, water, and oxygen from their environment and process these to yield energy for their activities and to provide building materials for their own growth and repair, discharging the unusable wastes and by-products back into the environment again. Like almost all organisms (plants as well as animals), they arise from parents like themselves, grow up to produce offspring of the same kind, and eventually die. (Very primitive organisms which reproduce by dividing into two are practically immortal, and there are animals as well as plants in which the offspring resemble not their parents but their grandparents or yet remoter ancestors, so that there is an alternation or cycle of generations often associated with a cycle of environmental conditions.)

Insects share with the higher vertebrates (birds, reptiles, and mammals, including man) another basic similarity —they are primarily land animals. Those which now live in the water are descended from land-dwelling ancestors. Land animals have physiological and anatomic problems unknown to creatures of the sea. They must avoid drying out. They must be able to support their own weight. They must be freely mobile, capable of hunting for food, shelter, and

A short-horned grasshopper

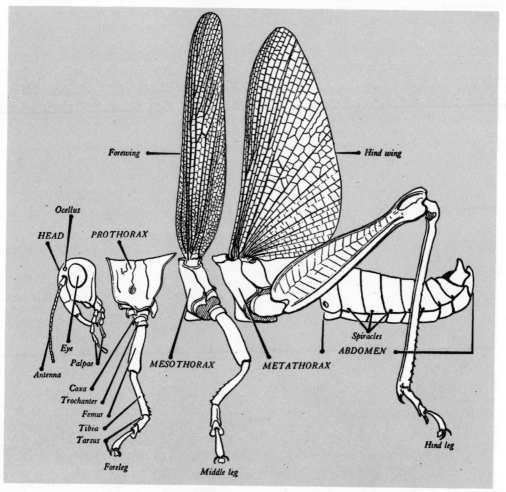

Topography of a grasshopper

a mate. (Water animals can drift with the current or remain anchored while the current brings them food and other of their needs.) They must be tolerant of changes of temperature and light intensity much greater and more rapid than sea creatures ever know, and capable of withstanding or avoiding unfavorable seasons. Being vertebrates ourselves, we know something about how vertebrates are constructed and how they contrive to live in harsh terrestrial environments. Insects meet the same needs with essentially similar physiological processes, but by means and methods so different that they are sometimes said to be upside down and inside out.

The most inside-out thing about insects is the position of the skeleton. It is not inside as the bones of vertebrates are, but outside in the form of a "shell" of horny or leathery plates with flexible joints between them. This armorlike skin not only supports the body while allowing it to move freely, it usually keeps water in as well. Some insects that live in wet places have water-permeable skins.

The insect's muscles are attached to the inside of its skeleton. They resemble the striated muscles of vertebrates, but the area available for their attachment is proportionally so much greater than that offered by the vertebrate skeleton that an insect is much stronger than a vertebrate of the same size would be. Comparisons of strength, based upon the relative size of an insect and a man, however, are unsound. The man is so much heavier that he has to use most of his strength just carrying himself. Strength increases by squares, weight by cubes. More remarkable than the strength of insect muscle is the rapidity with which it can contract—some tiny flies can beat their wings 1,000 times a second.

The outer part of the insect skin is of *chitin,* a nonliving secretion of the living epidermal cells beneath. Chitin is flexible. The stiff plates of the skeleton have been transformed by chemical reaction into a rigid substance called sclerotin. A "shell" of chitin and sclerotin does not grow. It can only spread a little at the joints. When it gets too tight, the epidermal cells secrete a fluid which dissolves the inner part of the nonliving material. Then they secrete a new layer of chitin.

At this time the epidermal cells grow and divide, so that the living part of the skin becomes larger, and the new layer of chitin is larger too. The whole skin is full of tiny wrinkles so that it fits inside the smaller "shell." At length, the insect swallows a lot of air, or water if it is an aquatic insect, and inflates itself like a balloon. The loosened "shell" splits, usually down the back, and the insect wriggles out. It must stay inflated, sometimes for hours, to keep its new "shell" stretched tight while it hardens. Almost always the new outer skin is pale and thin. It thickens and darkens gradually for days or even weeks. The whole process of skin-changing is called molting or *ecdysis.* All arthropods molt, many of them throughout their lives. Insects stop molting when they reach maturity. The number of times any one insect molts varies with species, often with sex, and not uncommonly with diet and other external influences. The interval between moltings is called an *instar.* There are insects which pass through as few as three instars during their lives, while others require twenty or more.

Closely associated with ecdysis is the phenomenon of regeneration. If an arthropod loses a leg or other appendage, it will grow a new one at its next molting. The new member will be smaller than normal, but it will become proportionally larger in each succeeding instar until the regeneration is complete. Since adult insects do not molt, the loss of an appendage is permanent when the insect is full-grown.

In most insects the primitive arthropod segmentation is still evident except in

A dragonfly emerges from its sh

USES OF LEGS

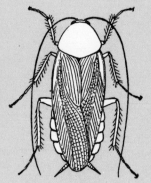

Running (cockroach)

Jumping (grasshopper)

Collecting (honey bee)

USES OF WINGS

Armor (lady beetle)

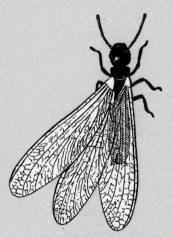

Mating flight (termite)

Foraging (butterfly)

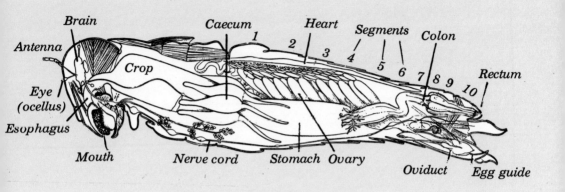

The internal anatomy of a typical insect

the head. Five segments have contributed to its formation, but the lines between them have been entirely obliterated. They are represented by their appendages. A pair of antennae, a pair of compound eyes, and three simple eyes mark the first segment. Some anatomists believe that the compound eyes represent the appendages of a separate segment because in crustacea they are mounted upon jointed stalks. If their belief is correct, there are six segments in the insect head. The second segment of the head once carried the second pair of antennae, but they have disappeared. We know they were there because they show briefly during the development of the embryonic insect inside the egg. The mandibles belong to the third segment, and the maxillae to the fourth. The second pair of maxillae, representing the fifth segment, have become fused together into a single organ called the *labium*, the insect's underlip, which closes the mouth behind. The *labrum*, or upper lip, is a flap of the head capsule that hangs down over the mouthparts in front: It was never a pair of legs. The maxillary and labial palpi resemble little feet at the sides of the mouth.

The thorax or midsection of the insect body is specialized for locomotion. It consists of three segments closely welded together but still distinct. Each bears a pair of jointed legs. The form of the legs varies greatly in insects of different habits. There are long legs for running, shovel-shaped legs for digging, paddle-shaped legs for swimming, springlike legs for leaping, basketlike legs for carrying pollen, traplike legs for grasping prey, and many other kinds. Typically, the second and third segments of the thorax each carry a pair of wings. However, either or both pairs may be absent or so shrunken that they no longer serve for flight. There are also other uses for insect wings. They may be gyroscopic **stabilizers, armor plate, musical instru**ments, aqualungs, or oars, for example.

An insect wing is an outgrowth of the body wall, rather like a pocket turned inside out. Usually it is thin and transparent like cellophane but strengthened by a framework of little tubes called veins. The number of the veins and the pattern that they assume are very constant within species and very similar in related species, so wing venation is often used in describing and classifying insects. The wings develop gradually, either inside or outside the body, as the insect grows, and become functional only in the final instar.

A flying insect is a full-grown insect. Some use their wings only in emergency or on special occasions such as a mating

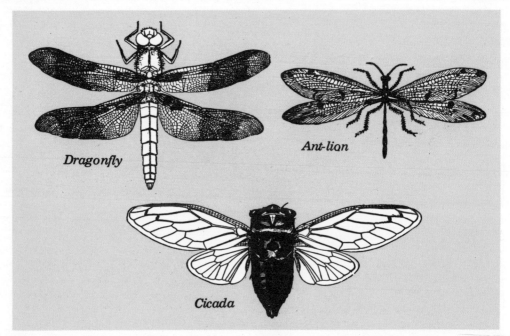

The vein patterns of insect wings are so distinct and constant that they are often used as identifying characters to separate one species from another

flight: Others use theirs regularly for foraging. A few make seasonal migrations over hundreds of miles (*See under Butterflies and Moths: Migration*). Not much is known about the ground speed of insect flight. Long ago a scientist reported, upon insufficient evidence which no one has been able to verify, that the deer botfly could outdistance a rifle bullet. That has never been disproved; but the greatest speeds of which insects can be shown to be capable are well within the speed limits established for cars on highways.

The third section of the insect body is the abdomen. It is a container for the viscera, the center of the functions of digestion, excretion, and reproduction. Most of the appendages have been lost. Those that remain are greatly reduced and so altered as to be almost unrecognizable as legs. The primitive number of segments was probably 12, but few modern insects have more than 10 and some have no more than 5. The segmentation is perfectly clear, each ring typically consisting of top and bottom plates with expansion joints between them on the sides.

The joints between the body segments are very flexible so that the rings telescope one within another when the abdomen is empty, or spread far apart when it is full. The number and uses of the abdominal appendages vary greatly among the different groups of insects. Feelers called *cerci* are often found at the rear end of the body: They are particularly conspicuous in cockroaches and mayflies. The springing apparatus of springtails is derived from abdominal legs. So are the *ovipositors*, or egg-placing tools, of many female insects and the claspers or mating forceps of many males. Some immature insects, notably caterpillars, have functional legs on their abdomens, but these legs are unsegmented. They are called abdominal prolegs to distinguish them from the segmented thoracic legs.

The upside-down thing about insects is the relative position of the heart and the central nerve cord. In vertebrates the nerve cord runs down the middle of the back while the heart is on the bottom or in front. In insects, the heart runs down the middle of the back and the nerve cord down the middle of the underside.

The insect central nervous system is still strongly segmental. It consists of a pair of cords lying side by side with a concentration of nerve cells—a ganglion —in each cord for each segment of the body. The two ganglia of each segment are closely connected, forming a sort of little brain that controls the activities of that segment. Sometimes, though not always, the three pairs of thoracic ganglia are fused into a single mass. The ganglia of the head segments are con-centrated into two masses, one above the esophagus, one below, connected by nerve cords around the sides. The underpart or subesophageal ganglion controls the mouthparts. The upper part or supraesophageal ganglion receives the nerves of the eyes and antennae and serves to coordinate the activities of the insect as a whole. This insect brain is assisted in its work of coordination by endocrine glands, located in various parts of the body, that act either directly or through the nervous system to control molting, maturation, and other physiological events.

The senses of insects are very acute, but strictly limited to the perception of things that have some bearing upon the particular insect's way of life. For ex-

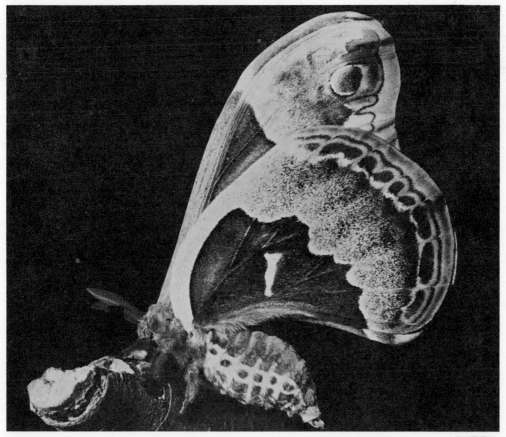

The cecropia moth can scent a female of the same species more than a mile away

ample, a male Saturnian moth can scent a female of the same species more than a mile upwind, but that is the only thing he can smell at all. It is the only thing that it is important for him to smell. The detection of other odors would be pointless, perhaps even a hindering distraction. All insects are sensitive to significant chemicals. The receptors are minute pits in the skin covered with delicate membrane and each served by a sensory nerve. They are widely scattered. Distance receptors — organs of scent — are most concentrated on the antennae. The larger an insect's antennae the keener is its sense of smell. Contact receptors —organs of taste—are most abundant on the mouthparts and on the feet, which first touch possible food.

Every insect's body is more or less densely clothed with bristles and smaller hairlike processes called *setae*. Many of them are set in sockets of flexible membrane and equipped with sensory nerves. These are tactile organs. Appropriately, they are particularly dense on antennae, mouthparts, cerci, and feet, which are most constantly in touch with the environment. Since the bristles move in response to the slightest pressure, they can sometimes detect sound waves too. Cockroaches, for example, hear sounds of high pitch with their antennae, and those at lower pitch with their cerci.

Insects that make use of sounds can certainly hear, and some of them have recognizable ears. The ears of a cricket are located on its front legs just below the knees. Those of a noctuid moth are on the sides of the thorax below the bases of the wings. Although moths are mute, their ears are attuned to the supersonic cries of bats, their mortal enemies.

The insect ear is a cavity covered by a tympanum or eardrum to the inside of which the auditory nerves are connected. Their nerves are so few that delicate discrimination of pitch by them is impossible. A cricket, for example, can detect sounds of a very wide range of wavelengths, but it cannot distinguish among them. What it does distinguish is the variation of intensity—a sort of very rapid Morse code "call letter" which varies with the species of cricket.

Insects that spend their lives in total darkness are often blind (*see under Cave Life*), but most kinds have excellent vision for their needs. Movement, indicated by change in the intensity of light, is perceived by insects more clearly than form. The clarity of the image seen by an insect depends upon the number and smallness of the individual units of the compound eyes. Each unit registers no more than a spot of light. The more spots there are, and the smaller, the more detail is possible in the "mosaic" which they form. (Try working out a picture by filling in the squares of graph paper of different grids, and you will see why.)

Insects that visit flowers are able to distinguish colors, though the range of their color perception is not quite like those of a human being. Bees can distinguish ultraviolet as a separate hue, but red is black to them. Some butterflies do perceive red. Not much is known about the color discrimination of insects in whose lives the ability to distinguish among wavelengths of light is usually unimportant.

The three simple eyes, or ocelli, are something of a mystery. Apparently they are more sensitive to changes of light intensity than are the compound eyes, and they act as starters to set the compound eyes to work. They do not seem to work by themselves. An insect with its ocelli covered reacts to light slowly. One with its compound eyes covered does not react to light at all.

Scattered all over the insect body, but particularly at the joints, are sense organs buried in the skin to register changes of pressure and tension caused by the movements of the animal. These are called *chordotonal organs*. (Human beings have somewhat similar ones in their muscles which tell us about our

The compound eyes of insects are composed of thousands of individual light receptors

movements; also temperature receptors scattered all over the skin.)

The circulatory system of insects is "open." The blood is not confined to arteries and veins but fills the entire body cavity. Insects make good use of hydraulic pressure. By contracting one part of the body they can force blood into another, causing it to expand. The heart is a segmented tube reaching from head to hind part. Between the segments are valves that permit the blood to pass in one direction only. Usually the flow is from back to front, but it can be reversed. In the sides of each segment are a pair of valves that allow blood to pass into the tubes but not out. Entering the heart at many places, the blood is forced out at one only, usually in the head, and works its way back among the organs at random. There are often little pulsating structures—accessory hearts—at the bases of legs, wings, or antennae to assure circulation in these narrow appendages.

Insect blood is colorless, pale yellow, or greenish, but almost never red. It serves for the transportation of useful chemicals and waste products, but has almost nothing to do with respiration. Its corpuscles are all white ones similar to those of vertebrates though of greater variety. The few insects that do have red blood live in water with little oxygen. The pigment is *haemoglobin* and it does have a respiratory function, but it is free in the plasma, not confined to corpuscles.

The respiratory system of insects consists of a complex network of tiny tubes that carry air directly from the surface to all parts of the body. Openings called spiracles, typically one pair on each segment, lead into a pair of comparatively large tubes, the main tracheal trunks, which run down the sides of the body. From these trunks, finer and finer tubes branch out in every direction, ending in microscopic blind *tracheoles*, the tips of which are filled with fluid. The actual interchange of oxygen and carbon dioxide takes place by diffusion through this liquid. The larger air tubes or tracheae are kept open and flexible by a lining consisting of a coiled thread of stiff chitin. This lining is part of the insect's skin and is shed every time the insect molts.

In insects, as in vertebrates, the digestive system is essentially a tube running the length of the body from mouth to anus. In insects, it is divided into three sections, the foregut, the midgut, and the hindgut, with regions specialized for the temporary storage, grinding, digestion, and absorption of food and for the accumulation and discharge of the useless residue. The details of its structure vary as greatly as do the food habits of the insects.

At the juncture of midgut and hindgut several pairs of fine tubules empty into the digestive tract. They may be long and coiled or short and branching, even tufted. These are the excretory organs of the insect, like the kidneys of vertebrate animals. They are called *Malpighian* tubules after the Italian scientist, Malpighi, who first described them almost three hundred years ago.

Most kinds of insects reproduce sexually, with male and female organs in separate individuals. There are, however, many species in which males are unknown, and at least one in which a single individual is both male and female at the same time. The reproductive systems of the two sexes are similar in plan. A pair of gonads—*ovaries* in the female, *testes* in the male—lie beside or below the digestive tract. Tubes leading from them meet in a single duct that opens near the tip of the abdomen below and in front of the anus. Attached to the duct are storage reservoirs for the reproductive cells and glands which produce secretions necessary for the transportation and well-being of the eggs and sperms.

Some insect sperms are extremely long-lived. A queen bee, once mated, remains fertile for years, drawing at

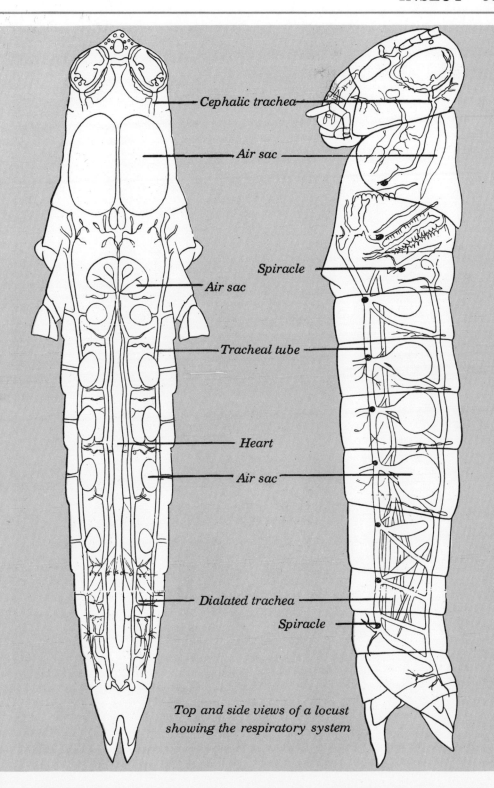

Cephalic trachea

Air sac

Air sac

Tracheal tube

Spiracle

Heart

Air sac

Dialated trachea

Spiracle

Top and side views of a locust showing the respiratory system

A monarch butterfly emerges from its chrysalis

need upon the sperms stored in her receptacle. In several groups of insects the males produce spermatophores—egg-like capsules or masses of jelly in which a large number of sperms are transferred to the female as a unit. The number of eggs produced by a female insect varies from a few dozens to perhaps a million, in a long lifetime. Sometimes they are all deposited at once, more often they are laid in small batches or singly over a period of days or months. Some female insects carry their eggs internally until they hatch and bear their young "alive." A very few retain the young and feed them on nourishing secretions until they are ready to mature. These are truly "live-bearing," though in a fashion very different from that of live-bearing vertebrate animals.

Around and between the other organs is a mass of soft white tissue—the fat body. This is the insect's reserve food supply, its starvation insurance and the source of energy for the periods of its life cycle during which it is unable to feed. In many species the fat body must even provide fuel and raw materials for the maturation of the reproductive cells and for all the activities of the adult insect. Adults of such species have no functional mouthparts and cannot feed. They are necessarily short lived.

Growth and Development

Most organisms undergo some change of form or at least of proportion during their individual development. This change is called *metamorphosis*. Insects are remarkable for the variability of the degree of metamorphosis which they exhibit. In some very primitive wingless insects the young resemble the adults in everything but size and the development of the reproductive system. Such species are said to be without metamorphosis. Among the winged groups, the more ancient ones have gradual metamorphosis. The young differ from the adults chiefly in the development of their wings. When they first hatch from the egg, they are small and wingless. By the time they are half grown, there are little flaps where the wings will be. These get larger and more winglike at every molt until they reach full size as the insects mature. The young of insects with gradual metamorphosis are called *nymphs*.

In the most recently evolved groups of insects metamorphosis is extreme and apparently sudden. The young do not look in the least like the adults and usually they live in different places and feed on different things. The more-or-less wormlike creature that emerges from the egg is called a *larva*. As it feeds and grows, wings do develop gradually, but inside, where they do not show. At length the full-fed larva molts to assume a new form—that of the *pupa* in which the wing pads are clearly visible. During the pupal stage the larval organs of the insect break down and the materials are reused in building organs of the adult type. While this is happening the insect is usually completely helpless and always unable to feed. When the reorganization is complete the pupal skin is shed and the fully winged adult insect emerges (*See Butterflies and Moths*).

More than any other one circumstance, the development of complete metamorphosis with division of labor between the active stages of the life cycle accounts for the success of insects in occupying almost every place on earth in which animals of any sort can live. The job of the adult is to provide for the next generation. Each can perform its task under conditions which would be intolerable to the other. It is hard to imagine any place so inhospitable that some insect cannot make use of it at one time or another.

The Family Lives of Insects

The great majority of insects have no family life. The parents cooperate only in the act of mating. The mother deposits her eggs in a place where her offspring will be able to live and find suitable food, and then abandons them. The adults are dead by the time the eggs hatch, and the baby insects are fully independent from the moment of hatching. There are, however, a good many kinds of insects in which the mother remains with the eggs until they hatch and the young have molted for the first time. In other species, the mother stores with each of her eggs enough food to last till the larva pupates. Many wasps and bees do this. It is the first step toward social life such as that of ants, hornets (*See Hornet*) and honeybees (*See under Bee*). In other wasps (hornets and wasps) the mother lives longer and is able to bring fresh food to her larvae as they grow, instead of storing it all at once ahead of time. This is another step toward social life.

In truly social insects the mother is very long lived. She rears her first brood to maturity herself. As the daughters mature they take over the work of caring for their younger sisters, and for brothers when there are any. The societies of ants, bees, and wasps are feminine. Males have no function other than reproduction, and are themselves, produced only at the breeding season. With termites, the only other social insects, this is not true. Individuals of both sexes take part in all the activities of the colony.

The mother in the truly social insect continues to lay eggs, but retires from other duties. The daughters, though female, seldom lay any eggs. Only during the breeding season do reproductive females develop. These leave the home nest to found new colonies. The daughters forage, enlarge the family home and keep it clean and in repair, groom and feed their mother, each other, and the larvae, and repel enemies that may try to enter the nest.

The activities of an insect colony often require the cooperation of many individuals. The insects have various ways of communicating with one another. Sounds are sometimes used, but touch and scent are more important, and even flavors help to keep the insect household together and working in harmony.

The Intelligence of Insects

Whether or not insects are intelligent at all depends upon the definition of intelligence that is applied to them. If we interpret intelligence as "the ability to learn and to know," then insects are extremely stupid. In so far as can be discovered, even the most complicated insect activities are performed unconsciously in response to a very elaborate system of cues, both external and internal. The insect is born with its responses "built in," it does not need to learn them and it does not know what it is doing or why. On the other hand, if intelligence is "the ability to modify behavior as the result of experience" — a definition used by students of animal psychology — some of the ants and bees are quite smart. A honeybee, for instance, learns to visit particular flowers only at the times when their nectar flow is greatest, and ignores those same blossoms at other hours of the day.

When we see an insect doing what we should do under the same circumstances if we were as small as an insect we are tempted to suppose that the insect is acting from the same reasons. This would be a serious mistake. The insect brain is so much simpler than ours; it is not capable of reasoning and its motives are physiological rather than intellectual. Nevertheless, there is a fundamental similarity in the activity-control systems of all animals, and a great deal may be learned about the basic nature of intelligence by the study of insect behavior.

The Hazards of Insect Life and How Insects Meet Them

The life of an insect is a risky one. Heat and cold, drought and flood take toll of the population. Enemies devour them. Parasites and microbial disease kill them. In favorable seasons, when not many die of other causes, the food supply may be insufficient and soon exhausted.

The ways in which insects meet the hazards of their existence are as numerous as the hazards themselves. Some survive by being strong, tough, and tolerant of change. An adult swallowtail butterfly dies at the touch of frost, but the pupa of the same species lives through a snowy winter in the open. An adult weevil may be so heavily armored that even an entomologist can scarcely force a pin through it.

Some insects escape by running away. One knows how difficult it is to catch a fly in the kitchen, and how a grasshopper springs up under one's feet and disappears before one has recovered from his astonishment. The monarch butterfly runs away from winter, migrating south like a bird (*See Butterfly Migration*).

Many insects avoid bad weather and enemies alike by hiding inside or under something, at least during hours or seasons of greatest peril. A few make shelters for themselves. Caddis fly larvae and bagworms carry their houses with them wherever they go. Many other larvae make cocoons or molting retreats that protect them during their period of helplessness.

Insects that live in the open and have enemies that hunt by sight are usually camouflaged. The walkingstick looks so much like a twig that one cannot see it even when one knows where to look. The katydid resembles in color and shape the leaves among which it lives.

Some insects are protected from enemies by offensive odors or flavors. Some carry weapons—stings, beaks, or poison sprays. Very commonly such protected insects are brightly colored. No bird or toad that has eaten one will want another, and the conspicuous coloring makes them easy to remember.

A few insects that are actually neither armed nor distasteful resemble protected species so closely that predators avoid them too. The viceroy butterfly looks almost exactly like the monarch, and birds which dislike the monarch leave it strictly alone. The wasp moth looks enough like a wasp to be safe from a toad which has once been stung. Mimicry, as it is called, works best when the protected model species is common and the mimic comparatively rare. Sometimes several equally well-protected species look alike, although not very closely related. It is an advantage to all of them that their common enemies should have only one color scheme to remember and avoid.

Insects in the Natural Community

Insects play a large and vital role in maintaining the balance of nature in terrestrial and freshwater habitats—there are virtually none in the sea. There are about 800 million known species, (plus or minus 200,000), of which roughly one tenth live in America north of Mexico. There are probably 8,000 species within easy collecting distance of any student with a car at his disposal. No two species of insects have exactly the same requirements, but among them they make use of everything the environment can offer. The majority, of course, feed upon plants. Others prefer the nectar or pollen of flowers. Some drink the sap. Others feed inside leaves (leaf miners), stems, fruits, roots, or seeds. While many insects feed upon plants that are living, many others prefer those that are dead, or even rotting. Indeed, the work of insects in breaking down dead vegetation and helping to return its elements to the soil for reuse is exceedingly important, particularly in tropical jungles.

Although insects are often destructive to plants, many plants, including hundreds of kinds of utmost value to man, owe their existence to insects. Bees, flies, butterflies, and other insects that go from flower to flower collecting nectar or pollen for their own use also carry pollen from one blossom to another,

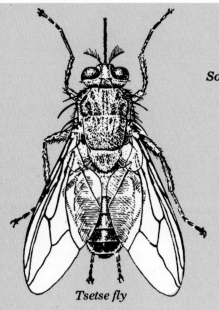

Some typical insects that cause disease in man

Tsetse fly

Sucking louse

assuring the setting of seed (*See Pollination*). Flowers and flower-visiting insects evolved together. Had there been no insects capable of visiting many flowers in succession, scented and brightly colored blossoms would never have evolved.

Plant-eating insects are the prey of countless carnivores—other insects, spiders, and centipedes among invertebrates, and such vertebrates as frogs, fishes, turtles, snakes, birds, and mammals, even including man. Man, in general, is the only animal that regards insects as inedible. In fact, insects are nourishing and flavorful human food. Where larger meat animals are scarce, insects are an important source of fat and protein in the human diet.

Carnivorous insects are themselves eaten by larger carnivores (*see Carnivore*) and some kinds prey upon creatures much larger than themselves. The largest animals may have lice, fleas, or internal insect parasites. Insect scavengers help to rid the world of the carcasses of dead animals of any size,

enriching the soil in the process.

Though insects are small, they are abundant, and in general, the smaller the species, the more numerous the individuals. An acre of rich grassland may support several hundred million insects small enough to pass through a window screen as well as hundreds of thousands of larger kinds. The density of the insect population depends largely upon the amount and kind of food available, the number of enemies present, and the accessibility of shelter during bad weather. Since none of these things remain constant, the insect population also varies from place to place and from year to year.

Insects and Man

Every plant or animal product that people raise and store for their own use is equally desirable to insects. Man's habit of cultivating and hoarding foods and other materials in huge quantities must naturally result in a huge increase in the population of such insects as feed upon those materials. In the natural course of events, one of two outcomes

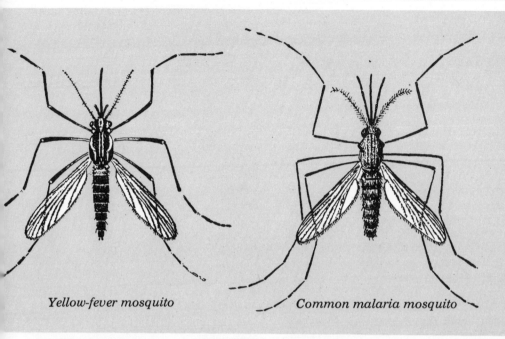

Yellow-fever mosquito　　　　　*Common malaria mosquito*

would be likely: (1) The insects would eat up all the food available and then starve to death; (2) the animals that feed on those insects (their own food supply having increased so greatly) would in turn multiply rapidly and check the increase of the pests.

In either case, the balance of insect, food supply, and of insect enemy (*see Insect Predators and Parasites*) would be restored. Man cannot afford to have it restored in the first manner, and is seldom willing to wait for the second to take effect. The alternative is to make the crop, herd, or food stores inedible by treating them with poisonous chemicals. The chemical chosen must be deadly or at least repellent to the pest insect in question, but preferably not so to other and possibly beneficial insects (*See Insecticide*). It should also be either harmless to people, pets, and domestic animals or so readily decomposed that it becomes harmless before the treated products are used. If the insecticide is to be applied over a wide area, the effect upon wildlife must also be considered. To complicate matters yet further, pest insects very quickly become resistant to insecticides. The first application may kill 95 percent of the pests. The surviving five percent bequeath to some of their descendents the hardiness that enabled them to withstand the poison, or the sensitivity that enabled them to avoid it. In the next generation, perhaps 20 percent will survive, and within a few years almost the whole population will be immune to the poison. The wise choice and successful application of chemicals for the control of insect pests requires a very thorough understanding of the pests, the chemicals, and the natural community in which the application must be made. Unskillful attempts at pest control may do more harm than good.

In addition to the insects which affect man indirectly there are some that attack him personally. Almost any insect that is large enough will bite if it is roughly handled. "Furry" caterpillars are often painful to touch (*See under Caterpillar*). Their hairs are brittle and sometimes filled with irritating fluid that enters the minute punctures made by the broken hairs and causes a burning or itching rash. Wasps, bees, and some ants sting vigorously in defense of their colonies. The sting is a converted ovipositor or egg-layer, so male insects never have them. Fleas, lice, bedbugs, kissing bugs, horseflies, blackflies, and mosquitoes are the most widespread and common of the insects that feed on blood. Annoying as their bites may be, they are trifling by comparison to the harm done by the disease microbes that the insects carry from one victim to another.

Any insect that feeds by preference upon human blood and that lives long enough to need several meals is likely to be a *vector,* or carrier of disease. Often, though not always, the microbe undergoes part of its life cycle within the insect and another part within its human host. (Domestic, and wild animals and plants as well, all fall victim to insect-borne diseases.) Fungal, bacterial, protozoan, and virus infections can all be transmitted by insect bites. Such infections are more common in the tropics than in temperate lands, and were more devastating in the past, when their causes were unknown, than they now are. Nevertheless, malaria, a protozoan disease carried by mosquitoes of the genus *Anopheles,* is the world's greatest public health problem in the present day. Other important insect-borne diseases are bubonic plague, carried by the rat flea; typhus, carried by lice; yellow fever, carried by mosquitoes *Aedes aegypti;* and African sleeping sickness, carried by the tsetse fly. There are many more (*See Arbovirus*).

An outbreak of insect-borne disease can occur only when microbe, insect, and susceptible human beings are all present in the same place at the same time. Removal of any one of the three organisms brings the epidemic to an end. Perhaps the microbe can be killed with drugs while in its human host, but most of the disease microbes have wild animal hosts as well, and that

makes microbe eradication impractical. Screens help keep people out of reach of infected insects. It is much more effective to make people immune, either through survival of infection or by inoculation. If everyone who has not already had the disease can be vaccinated against it, nobody will catch it. Killing the insect vector is another valuable way of fighting an epidemic. It can be done efficiently only when the life cycle and habits of the insect are thoroughly understood. Then the control measures can be applied to the insect in the stage of development in which it is most easily found and killed. For example, if one knows that a certain mosquito passes its larval stage only in small bodies of standing fresh water, he can get rid of it by filling puddles, draining ditches, screening rain barrels, and burying tin cans that might trap rain water. If one has ponds or pools that he does not want to drain, he can stock them with some mosquito-eating fishes. Where there is no place for the larvae to live there will be no adults to bite one. Any or all of these methods can be used to prevent an epidemic of insect-borne disease or to bring one under control.

The Classification of Insects

There are so many kinds of insects that no one can possibly remember them all, but anyone can see that some kinds are more or less alike and more or less different from other kinds. It is assumed that the degree of similarity is a clue to relationship. Shared characteristics are usually inherited from a common ancestor, and the more of them there are the more closely the creatures that have them are related. On the basis of hereditary similarities, insects are classified into a series of progressively larger categories. For example, a population of individuals so similar that any pair can produce fertile offspring is a species. Scientists say "a species is a reproductively isolated population." If two otherwise similar populations live in the same place and are capable of interbreeding but do not do so because they happen to be active at different times of day, or for any other reason, then they are two separate species.

Species that are very much alike constitute a genus.

Genera that are very similar make up a family.

Related families form an order.

The class Hexapoda comprises all the orders of insects.

Orders are distinguished largely by the type of life cycle through which their members pass, and the structure of the mouthparts and the wings.

Because scholars do not always agree about the importance of observed differences between groups of insect families, there is some uncertainty about the number of orders into which insects should be divided, but most textbooks of entomology list about 25. Anyone can easily learn to recognize the order of almost any adult insect he may happen to meet.

The Subclass Apterygota.

These are the totally wingless orders,

CLASSIFICATION OF INSECTS

Kingdom Animal
   Phylum Arthropoda—Segmented invertebrates with jointed legs
     Subphylum Mandibulata—Arthropods with mandibles on the second posteral somite
      Class Hexopoda
       Subclass Apterygota—Wingless insects. One percent of the total insect   population
         Order Protura—Insects without antennae
         Order Thysanura—Bristle-tailed insects, i.e., silverfish, firebrat
         Order Collembola—Springtails
       Subclass Pterygota—Insects with wings in the adult stage or with winged   ancestors
        Superorder Exopterygota—Insects with incomplete metamorphosis and wings that
                develop externally; 12 percent of the insect population
         Order Ephemeroptera—Mayflies
         Order Odonata—Dragonflies and Damselflies
         Order Orthoptera—Mantids, cockroaches, grasshoppers, crickets, walkingsticks,
             katydids
         Order Isoptera—Termites
         Order Plecoptera—Stone flies
         Order Dermaptera—Earwigs
         Order Embioptera—Embiids
         Order Psocoptera—Psocids
         Order Zoraptera—Zorapterans
         Order Mallophaga—Chewing lice
         Order Anoplura—"True," or sucking lice
         Order Thysanoptera—Thrips
         Order Hemiptera—Insects with jointed beaks
           Suborder Heteroptera—True bugs
           Suborder Homoptera—Cicadas, leafhoppers, treehoppers, aphids, etc.
        Superorder Endopterygota—Insects with complete metamorphosis. Wings do not
                develop externally in larval stages. Eighty-seven per-
                cent of the total insect population
         Order Neuroptera—Lacewings, fish flies, alder flies, dobsonflies, snake flies
         Order Coleoptera—Beetles
         Order Strepsiptera—Twisted-winged insects, usually small parasites of other
              insects
         Order Mecoptera—Scorpion flies
         Order Trichoptera—Caddisflies
         Order Lepidoptera—Moths and butterflies
         Order Diptera—"True," or two-winged flies
         Order Siphonaptera—Fleas
         Order Hymenoptera—Sawflies, horntails, ichneumon "flies," gall wasps, hornets,
              bees, ants, etc.

primitive insects descended with little change from forms that existed before wings had evolved. The young are practically perfect miniatures of the adults and have similar habits. About one percent of the known species of insects are apterygote.

The order Protura. Proturans are the only insects without antennae, and the only ones in which the number of segments in the abdomen increases during growth. The hatchling has 9 abdominal segments, the adult 12. They are slender animals only about a tenth of an inch long and often transparent. They live in the soil and among decaying vegetation. Though common in nature they are rare in collections because they are so easily overlooked.

The order Thysanura. (This group is sometimes broken into several orders.) The thysanurans are commonly called bristletails because of the two or three long hairlike projections at the rear end. Most of them live in dark, damp, sheltered places outdoors, but two species— the silverfish and the firebrat—are common household pests.

The order Collembola. Collembolans are distinguished by possession of an adhesive organ in the underside of the first abdominal segment—a little tube through which a sticky balloonlike structure protrudes when needed. Most collembola also have a forked "tail" which is bent forward under the body and fastened by a clasp on the third segment. When the clasp is released, the spring straightens out and the insect leaps. The name springtails is applied to the whole order, whether appropriate or not. Collembolans are often extremely abundant in the soil and among rotting vegetation. Occasionally they damage living plants, particularly cultivated mushrooms. The snow flea, one of the very rare insects that is active in the winter, is a collembolan, not a flea.

The Subclass Pterygota.

These are the orders in which most species are winged in the adult stage. Those species that do not now have wings are believed to be descended from winged ancestors. Loss of the wings is usually associated with ways of life in which wings would be a handicap.

The Superorder Exopterygota.

In this group metamorphosis is gradual and the wings develop on the outside of the body. About 12 percent of the known species of insects are exopterygote. They are divided into not less than 14 orders— sometimes as many as 18.

The order Ephemeroptera. These are the mayflies, famous for their huge mating swarms and for the brevity of their adult life. The nymphs live in the water, sometimes for several years; the adults seldom live more than two or three days, often less. Both stages are important foods for freshwater fishes.

Mayflies provide the only exception to the rule that no insect can fly before it is fully mature. Mayflies molt once more, a few hours after they emerge from the water and fly to some perch on the shore. The preadult stage is called the subimago. Its appendages are shorter and its wings less transparent than those of the *imago,* or adult.

The order Odonata. Dragonflies and damselflies are large, handsome, and beneficial insects. They are usually seen near ponds and lakes in which their nymphs live. Both stages are predatory upon other insects and destroy enormous numbers of mosquitoes and other pests.

The most curious characteristic of the Odonata is the head-to-tail attitude assumed by mating pairs flying "in tandem." Exceptional, too, is the fact that the male often helps his mate with her egg-laying. Sometimes he keeps hold of her and pulls her up out of the water every time she dips under to deposit an egg on the bottom. Sometimes he stands by and drives away other males which

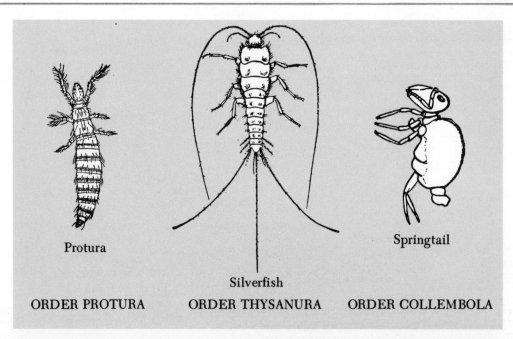

Protura

Silverfish

Springtail

ORDER PROTURA ORDER THYSANURA ORDER COLLEMBOLA

Mayfly ORDER EPHEMEROPTERA

might interrupt the egg-laying.

The nymphs of Odonata have remarkable hinged jaws which shoot forward like lazy tongs to grasp their prey. Dragonfly nymphs swim by jet propulsion. Their gills are not external, but are housed in the enlarged rear part of the rectum. By taking water into this gill chamber and squirting it out through partially closed valves, the insect jerks forward suddenly. This seems to be a means of escape from enemies. The dragonfly nymphs do not chase their own prey, but stalk it slowly or lie in ambush waiting for it to blunder near them.

The order Orthoptera. This great group includes grasshoppers, crickets, katydids, cockroaches, mantids, and walkingsticks—all the insects with leathery front wings and membranous, fan-pleated hind wings. It is sometimes divided into four separate orders, and one order includes the insects in which the hind legs are enlarged for jumping.

The jumping orthoptera are musicians. Their sounds (stridulations) attract other members of the same species, particularly prospective mates. Though not all females are mute, the noisy "songster" is almost always a male. Grasshoppers and katydids "sing" by rubbing a scraper on one front wing over a file on the other. Some short-horned grasshoppers rasp a row of pegs on the hind legs against the front wings.

The jumping orthoptera are chiefly plant-eaters, and some of them are extremely destructive agricultural pests. The plague locusts, notorious since ancient times, are short-horned grasshoppers (*See Grasshopper, and under Locust*).

Cockroaches differ from other orthopterans in the shield which covers the head, in the manner in which the wings overlap when folded, and in their willingness to eat anything. They are the most ancient living group of winged insects having remained almost unchanged since the coal age, about 300 million years ago. A few species are household pests, but most of them live outdoors, chiefly in the tropics (*See Cockroach*).

Walkingsticks too are commoner in the tropics than in temperate regions. Those found in the continental United States are nearly or entirely wingless. The winged species of other lands often look like leaves rather than twigs. They all feed upon foliage.

Mantids (praying mantises) are as well camouflaged as walkingsticks, but they are all predatory, feeding chiefly upon other insects. There is a persistent belief that the big Chinese mantis now so common in the northeastern United States was introduced for the purpose of fighting the Japanese beetle, and that there is a fine of twenty-five dollars for killing one. This is not true. The insect was introduced accidentally, it does not eat Japanese beetles if anything else is available, and it is in no need of the protection of the law. The front legs of a mantis are enlarged and edged with spines, forming a formidable trap for prey; and the front segment of the thorax is correspondingly elongated. Its little triangular head is mounted upon slender flexible neck. No insect but a mantis can look over its own shoulder (*See under Mantid*).

The order Isoptera. Termites are the only social insects with gradual metamorphosis. The nymphs are all workers, and in most species there are adult workers as well. Other working nymphs mature into soldiers or into primary or secondary reproductives—the so-called kings and queens. Most members of the colony are ivory-colored, but the primary reproductive members are dark, and they alone have functional wings. The wings are used only once, on the mating flight—the only time when termites voluntarily come out of their nests into the light. After the flight, the wings fall off, and each mated pair tries to begin a new colony (*See Termite*).

Black-wing damselfly ORDER ODONATA

All the termites in America north of Mexico feed upon wood. Many tropical species are fungus gardeners, and some of them make huge nests above ground. It is a curious fact that termites cannot digest the cellulose of which their food is largely composed. Protozoans living in the digestive systems of the insects do it for them.

Termites are often called white ants, but the name is misleading. They are really a great deal more like cockroaches than like ants. When "swarming," the reproductive forms of ants and termites do look somewhat alike, but it is easy enough to distinguish them if you look closely. A termite has two pairs of wings of equal length. (The very name Isoptera means *equal wings.*) Its waist is broad, like that of a roach, and its antennae are like tiny strings of beads, with all the segments similar in size. An ant has front wings much larger and longer than the back wings. Its waist is narrow, like that of a wasp, and its antennae are elbowed, with one very long segment at the base and a tip composed of many small segments set onto it at an angle (*See Ant*).

The order Plecoptera. Stonefly nymphs are often found under stones in running water, and the adults are usually seen clinging to stones or tree trunks on the banks of lakes or streams. Some species mature during the winter, and are active on sunny days while there is snow on the ground.

The order Dermaptera. The body of an earwig is long and flexible (*See Earwig*). Its front wings are short and leathery, and the big membranous hind wings fold up to fit under them. At the tip of the abdomen is a large pair of pincers.

There is an ancient belief that earwigs enter the ears of sleeping people. It is true that they are nocturnal, and that they hide by day in crevices. It is also true that they occasionally invade houses. It is not true that they have any preference for the human ear. Most of them are scavengers, though some do damage cultivated plants.

Earwigs are among the few insects in which the parent takes any care of the young. In an underground nest the mother stands guard over her eggs, and the family remains together for a short while after the eggs have hatched.

The order Embioptera. Colonies of these little cylindrical insects live together in silken tunnels among decaying vegetation or under stones or bark. Other insects spin silk, but only the embiids do it with their front feet. Females are wingless; males sometimes have wings that fold flat against the body.

Embiids feed chiefly on soft plant materials. Most species are tropical. There are a few in the southern and western United States, but they are not common enough to have an English name.

The order Psocoptera. Psocids are similar to aphids or "plant lice" (*see Aphid*) in size and shape, but have chewing mouthparts instead of sucking beaks. They feed on a great variety of soft and decaying material. A few kinds sometimes invade damp houses, but do little damage. These are wingless and are known as book lice. Most species live outdoors among leaf litter on the ground or on tree trunks and among vegetation. These usually have wings, and are called bark lice. The wings are sometimes short and very rarely the hind pair are absent.

The order Zoraptera. Zorapterans look like miniature roaches or termites, not more than an eighth of an inch long. They live together in colonies under bark or in rotting wood. The adults develop wings but soon shed them. So far as known, zorapterans are scavengers.

This is a tiny order. It contains only one family which consists of a single genus of 16 known species. Two are found in the southeastern United States.

Katydid   ORDER ORTHOPTERA

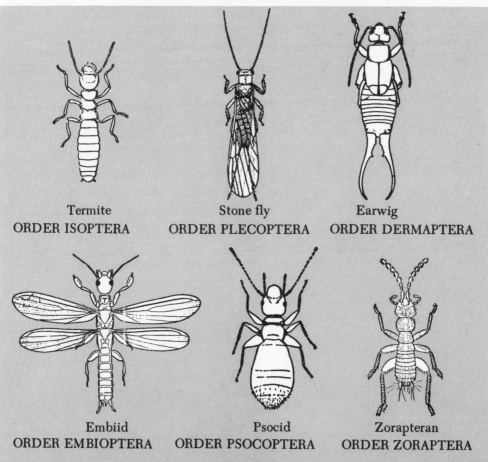

Termite
ORDER ISOPTERA

Stone fly
ORDER PLECOPTERA

Earwig
ORDER DERMAPTERA

Embiid
ORDER EMBIOPTERA

Psocid
ORDER PSOCOPTERA

Zorapteran
ORDER ZORAPTERA

The order Mallophaga. These little wingless insects are all external parasites on warm-blooded animals, chiefly birds, so they are sometimes called bird lice (*See under Parasite: Some Insect Parasites of Birds*). They have chewing mouthparts and feed upon bits of hair, feathers, and skin, so they are also called chewing lice. They are very common pests of poultry and domestic animals, and irritate their hosts so much that the host animals fall easy victims to disease. Each species of mallophagan infests a particular kind of host. Fortunately, none of them prefer man.

The order Anoplura. These are the "true" lice or sucking lice. They are all external parasites of mammals, feeding on blood. Two of them attack man. Wherever people are crowded together so that the wingless lice can walk from one to another, the insects are dangerous because of the disease microbes that they can spread as they feed. Typhus or "jail fever" is one of the diseases transmitted by lice.

The order Thysanoptera. Thrips are tiny insects with sucking mouthparts that feed on the juices of plants. They are often serious pests, less because of the direct damage they do than because of the plant diseases they transmit. Some species are wingless. When wings are present, they have fringes of long hair unlike those of any other insects.

Thrips are remarkable for their complicated life cycles of the two suborders. Despite differences, both types are intermediate between gradual and complete metamorphosis. The early instars are endopterygote—larvae with wing buds developing internally. The latter instars are exopterygote — with external wing pads—like a nymph or a pupa, and like a pupa, they do not feed. The final instar is the adult.

The order Hemiptera. With 55,000 species, this is by very far the largest of all the orders with gradual metamorphosis. Members have mouthparts in the form of a jointed beak. The group is divided into two suborders, often considered separate orders, distinguished by the position of the beak and the form of the wings.

The suborder Heteroptera comprises the "true" bugs. These have the beak arising on the front of the head and reaching back between the bases of the legs when not in use (*See under Bug*). The front wings are leathery at the base but membranous at the tip, the hind wings entirely membranous. When folded, the wings overlap and lie flat on top of the back. Heteropterans feed upon the sap of plants and the blood of animals. The bedbug, though wingless, is a heteropteran. Many are serious pests and the vectors of disease. A few use solid foods by a process of external digestion, injecting saliva into it and sucking up the resultant broth.

The *suborder Homoptera* comprises cicadas, leafhoppers, treehoppers, spittlebugs, aphids, whiteflies, scale insects, and many others. They all have beaks arising from the back of the head. The front wings may be either leathery or membranous, but they are of one texture all over. The back wings are membranous. When at rest, the wings meet in the middle of the back and resemble a pitched roof. There are many wingless species, and some species in which only one sex has wings.

All homopterans feed on the sap of plants, and some are pests and vectors of disease. On the other hand, a few yield commercially valuable products. Probably the most important of these is shellac, the secretion of a scale insect that lives on the twigs of trees in Asia.

The super-order Endopterygota.

These are the orders of insects in which the metamorphosis is complete. There are only 9 to 12 of them, and some of them are small, but the others are enormous. Eighty-seven percent of the known species of insects are endopterygote.

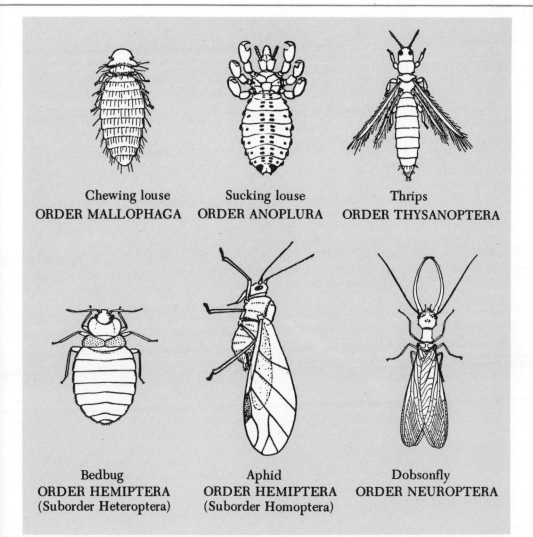

Chewing louse
ORDER MALLOPHAGA

Sucking louse
ORDER ANOPLURA

Thrips
ORDER THYSANOPTERA

Bedbug
ORDER HEMIPTERA
(Suborder Heteroptera)

Aphid
ORDER HEMIPTERA
(Suborder Homoptera)

Dobsonfly
ORDER NEUROPTERA

The order Neuroptera. This is a rather mixed lot of insects with four large wings netted with many veins. It is often divided into three orders.

One group includes lacewing "flys", ant-lions, and their close cousins—the Neuroptera in the narrow sense. One includes fish flies, alderflies, and dobsonflies—the Megaloptera—that are aquatic in the larval stage. One consists of the curious long "necked" snake flies, Raphidiodea. (The "neck" is really the front segment of the thorax which is elongated.)

Most neuropterans prey upon other insects, both as larvae and as adults. Many of the larvae have large hollow jaws through which they suck the juices of their victims. Most of them make silken cocoons. Their silk glands are modified Malphighian tubules, and the thread is spun at the rear of the body rather than from the mouth, as in caterpillars.

The order Coleoptera. These are the beetles, the largest of all orders of animals, roughly 277,000 species. About one-tenth of them live in North America. Beetles are distinguished from other insects by the horny or leathery front wings that meet in a straight line down the middle of the back and usually completely hide the hind wings that are folded underneath. Sometimes the front wings are short. Occasionally the hind wings are absent. It is very rare for a beetle to be entirely wingless (See Beetle).

The mouthparts of beetles are of the chewing type. They feed upon almost everything that has ever been alive. Plant-eaters like the Japanese beetle are often serious pests. Predators like the vedalia (a ladybug) are valuable in the control of destructive insects. A few beetles feed upon pollen or nectar and help to pollinate flowers (See Pollination). Beetle scavengers are very efficient in ridding the world of dead animals and dung.

The larvae of beetles vary greatly in appearance, and some forms have common names such as grub and wireworm. Like the adults, they live almost everywhere and eat almost everything.

Beetles are practically never parasitic. One which lives on beavers is a startling curiosity (See Beaver).

The order Strepsiptera. This is a small group of minute insects that are sometimes called twisted-winged insects. Most of them are parasites upon other insects. The adult males are always free-living and have large fanlike hind wings, but their front wings are mere paddles. Their eyes and antennae are large. The females are always wingless. Those that are parasites often lack legs, eyes, and antennae as well. They are mere egg-laying machines, which never leave their hosts.

The most fully parasitic strepsipterans are the most perfectly adapted internal parasites among insects. A well-adapted internal parasite should not kill its host, for that would force the parasite to find another home. Most parasitic insects do kill their hosts, but it does not matter to them because by that time they have completed their larval development, and the adults are not parasites. When the adult female strepsipteran is parasitic, she must allow her host to live at least until her young that are "born alive," have escaped through the skin of the host, and the mother has come to the end of her own life. The presence of the strepsipteran does the host no good, but it is not necessarily fatal to it.

The order Mecoptera. Scorpion flies (See Scorpion Fly) have faces elongated into beaks with chewing mouthparts at the tips. Their four wings are similar in size and shape. In males the tip of the abdomen turns up like the tail of a scorpion, but the insects are completely harmless. One family of wingless scorpion flies are among the few insects active during the winter. They feed on mosses. Members of another family hang by their front legs from twigs and use their hind legs to catch flies and other small insects for food.

The order Trichoptera. Adult caddis flies (see Caddis Fly) look like small moths, but their wings are hairy rather than scaly and their mouthparts are of the chewing type rather than sucking tubes like those of moths. The adults are seen near ponds, lakes, and streams in which their larvae live, and they often are attracted to lights at night.

The larvae of caddis flies (called caddisworms), are very like caterpillars, though their jointed legs are longer and they have no abdominal prolegs. Most of them make portable "houses" of silk and bits of sand, leaves, or twigs. Each species of caddisworm has its own favorite building material and builds cases of a characteristic shape. Some of them are coiled like snail shells, some oval, some cylindrical. The cases serve as cocoons when the larvae have finished growing. The pupa has powerful mandibles with which it cuts its way out of the case when the time comes for it to

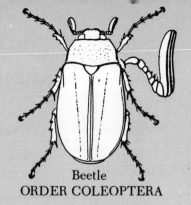

Beetle
ORDER COLEOPTERA

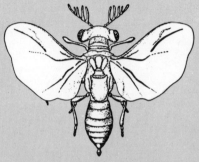

Twisted-winged insects
ORDER STREPSIPTERA

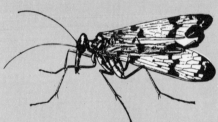

Scorpion flies
ORDER MECOPTERA

Caddis fly
ORDER TRICHOPTERA

swim ashore where the adult will emerge.

Several species of caddisworms spin little silken nets between stones on the bottom of a stream. They feed upon bits of plant and animal materials carried into their nets by the current.

The order Lepidoptera. These are the moths and butterflies—the insects clothed with tiny colored scales that come off like dust on your fingers. There are well over 100,000 species in the world, about 10,000 in the continental United States (*See Butterflies and Moths*).

The mouthparts of adult lepidoptera form a sipping straw through which they drink the nectar and sap of plants and such other nourishing fluids as the juice of carrion. When not in use, the long tongue is coiled up under the head like a watch spring. Some adult moths have no functional mouthparts and do not feed at all. While visiting flowers to drink the nectar, moths and butterflies bring about the pollination of the blossoms. Very deep trumpet-shaped flowers are usually pollinated by moths rather than by the relatively short-tongued bees.

The larvae of lepidoptera are caterpillars. They have chewing mouthparts and feed on almost everything of vegetable origin. Many are serious pests of agricultural crops and stored foodstuffs (*See Caterpillar*). Carnivorous caterpillars, for example those of clothes moths, are rare.

The order Diptera. The "true" or two-winged flies are another of the giant orders of insects (*See under Fly, and under Mosquito*). About one fifth of the world's eighty five thousand known species live in North America. They are almost all small soft-bodied insects. Only the front pair of wings are used for flying. The back pair have become reduced to stalked knobs that act as stabilizers. The mouthparts of flies are of several forms, but all are adapted for drinking liquids. Their food includes

Swallowtail butterfly   ORDER LEPIDOPTERA

nectar, sap, plant juices, and the blood of other insects or vertebrate animals. Many, like the mosquitoes, horseflies, and blackflies, bite people and spread the microbes that cause serious diseases.

The larvae of flies are usually legless. Some have tiny heads which can be pulled back into the body so that they disappear. Such larvae are called *maggots*. Nearly all fly larvae are thin-skinned and obliged to live in moist sheltered places. Some are borers in living plants or in dead logs. Some tunnel in the ground. Some are internal parasites of animals and many are aquatic.

Fly larvae do not make cocoons. Some pupae are naked. Others are formed inside the last larval skin, which hardens and darkens to become a brown capsule called a *puparium*.

The order Siphonaptera. Adult fleas are all external parasites (ectoparasites) upon warm-blooded animals. They are small, tough, wingless, and flattened sideways so that they slip easily between the hairs of their hosts (*See under Flea*). The back legs are enlarged for leaping. They often leave their hosts between meals and are not very particular about the kind of animal they bite. That is a big reason for their significance as carriers of disease. The rat flea, for example, carries bubonic plague from rats to people.

Flea larvae are slender, white "worms." They usually live in the nest of the animal upon which the parent adults feed. Their chief food is the excrement of adult fleas. When ready to pupate, they spin cocoons of silk.

The order Hymenoptera. This is a huge order, and a varied one. It includes sawflies, horntails, ichneumon "flies," or ichneumon wasps, gall wasps, hornets, bees, ants, and many others to the number of more than 100,000 species. About 15,000 occur in North America.

When wings are present, they are membranous. The front pair is larger

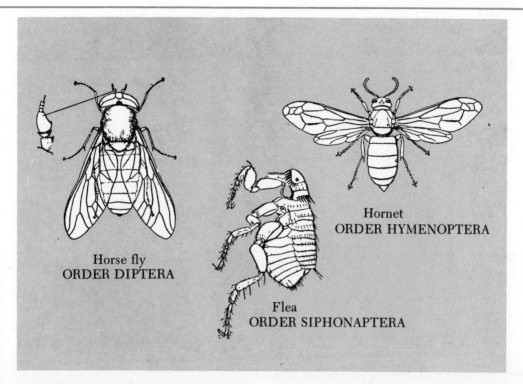

Horse fly
ORDER DIPTERA

Flea
ORDER SIPHONAPTERA

Hornet
ORDER HYMENOPTERA

than the back pair. On the front edge of the back wing is a row of tiny hooks which fit over a fold at the back edge of the front wing and fasten the two together when in use. The mouthparts are of the chewing type, but in many hymenoptera they are adapted for sucking also. Most of the food is liquid.

The hymenoptera are divided into two groups, of which the sawflies and horntails are thick-waisted; the others are narrow-waisted.

The larvae of thick-waisted wasps are like caterpillars, but usually have at least one more pair of abdominal prolegs than the caterpillars. Many of them curl up like a millipede when alarmed (*See Millipede*). Almost all of the larvae of the sawflies and horntails feed upon plants.

The larvae of narrow-waisted wasps are like maggots or the grubs of some beetles; pale, legless, sometimes almost headless. Among them some are borers and miners, others are gallmakers, internal parasites, and many depend upon their mothers for the provisions that they need for their development.

Social hymenoptera—some wasps, and some bees, and all of the ants—are the most advanced of all invertebrate animals. They live in family groups within which there is a division of labor among individuals of different types. Members of a colony communicate with one another and are capable of cooperation in carrying out tasks. So similar are their societies to human communities that it seems unlikely that their behavior should be altogether unconscious, however, scientists have not yet discovered it to be otherwise.

Hymenoptera are certainly the most useful of insects, from the human point of view: wasps because of the countless insects they kill that are destructive to man's interests; bees because of the wax and honey man gets from them, and because of their invaluable work in pollinating fruit, vegetables, ornamental flowers, and plants that yield drugs, fibers, and other useful products. —A.G.

Insects in the Classroom

Live insects are often dramatic, easy to get, and simple to keep. They come in an amazing variety of shapes, sizes, and colors. They are common in everyday life, yet the concern of eminent scientists. Although they compete with man for food upon this earth, they actually make food possible by their services as pollinators and soil builders. They nourish the songbirds and the freshwater gamefish. Insect lives touch upon men's lives at more points than any other animal group.

By keeping live insects where they can be watched every day, many things can be learned about them: how they grow, how and what they eat, the kind of environment they need, their relation to other living things—both plant and animal—their protective coloring, and other interesting adaptations.

It is not necessary to have expensive equipment to keep live insects; common household articles, assembled beforehand, will do. A few wide-mouthed jars will serve as well as battery jars for moisture-loving insects. The screw tops should be perforated to let in air. A number of old jelly tumblers, pint milk bottles, or preserve jars will do as temporary aquariums for water insects. Squares of gauze held in place with rubber bands or inverted draw-string bags may be used to prevent their escape. A strip of fly screening, about one foot high and held in the shape of a drum with paper clips at the overlapping edges, will make a cage for caterpillars or flying insects. The bottom of the drum should be inserted in a wooden flat filled with damp sand or earth to hold the screening erect and also to keep sprays of food plants upstanding and in good condition. An inverted shallow pan, a thin piece of wood, or a sheet of glass can be placed on top for a cover. Small insects may even be kept on slim food plants growing in flowerpots, a cotton-stopped lamp chimney being used to confine them.

Except for aquatic insects, it is not necessary or even desirable to have a dish of water in the cage. Insects do not require it and they are liable to drown if they have it. Moisture should be provided almost daily, however, either by lightly sprinkling the foliage or inside of each cage, or by providing a narrow-necked bottle of water, standing upright, with a cotton wick as a dispenser. The wick should fit tightly enough to prevent insects crawling inside the bottle and should be long enough to extend from the bottom of the bottle to an inch or more above the neck. Too much moisture is disastrous, especially for sun-loving insects; therefore one should be conservative with water until experience indicates just the amount to use.

Sanitation is important. The prompt removal of accumulated waste, of dead or moldy insects, food or plant parts is the surest road to success. A long pair of forceps is handy for this purpose, but two flat sticks will do if one is deft at using chopsticks.

Most fertile insect eggs will hatch and most cocoons or chrysalises will produce where the humidity is high (75 percent average) and where the temperature ranges from 70° to 85° F. A dry atmosphere leads to failure. The rate of emergence can be somewhat accelerated or retarded by increasing or decreasing the temperature from a mean of 75° F. Eggs and immature stages of insects can be held inactive for days, even months, in temperatures from 38° to 42° F.

Moisture-loving Insects

Cockroaches make good subjects for study even though most people want to get rid of them. They come of ancient lineage. No doubt their forefathers ran between the legs of giant dinosaurs when the earth was still hot and humid. Their breeding habits, egg-carrying habits, and responses to light, heat, and moisture are worth noting. Should they breed in too great numbers, they make excellent food for frogs, toads, and small lizards.

Cockroaches are of many kinds, but the so-called American roach, *Periplaneta americana,* and the German roach, or Croton bug, *Blattella germanica,* are the most satisfactory to raise and usually the easiest to get. They can either be trapped at night in a wooden box, fitted with a funnelway for easy entrance but difficult exit, or arrangements may be made with a professional exterminator to provide a few desirable specimens. Keep them in a glass container, where it is damp and warm, and smear vaseline around the inside upper edge to discourage escape of the lively beasts. When not under observation, they should be covered with a perforated lid as an added precaution against escape, and placed where it is dark. Under no conditions should they be exposed to sunlight.

The floor of the container should be kept mildly damp at all times. This is easiest accomplished when it is carpeted with fine sand, paper toweling, newspapers, moss, or blotting paper. Bottle caps filled with water may be inserted for long weekends, if this seems necessary. Bent twigs, crumpled paper, or curved sections of tree bark inside the container will furnish cover and climbing room as well as tend to discourage cannibalism.

For food, cockroaches relish most kinds of table scraps (moist bread, cake, raw bits of apple and other fruits, lettuce, and other greens), or moist dog biscuits and fig newtons. A small amount of raw meat may be given occasionally but it is apt to make them savage. The portions of any food given at one time should be small or it will spoil before being consumed.

The eggs of these cockroaches are contained in little brown capsules, which may often be seen protruding from the end of the mother's body before she has found a secluded spot in which to deposit them. The capsules should be removed to special breeding jars, supplied with damp, absorbent material at the bottom; otherwise they may be attacked by ravaging adults. Once the eggs have hatched; the young nymphs generally can run with their elders and share food without mishap.

Black field crickets, *Gryllus assimilis,* flourish in very much the same type of environment as that recommended for cockroaches, but because they lay their eggs in the ground, each cage should be provided with at least one inch of sand. If a decayed piece of wood is kept saturated with moisture and elevated on two stones above the drier sand, male crickets will mount the wood and chirp lustily with their wings in broad daylight just as they are accustomed to do at night. But they should not be placed in the sun. If confined in a jar more than eight inches tall, they need not be covered, since they cannot jump out; and an uncovered jar is less apt to develop mold.

Obtaining black field crickets is not a difficult task. In warm weather they generally can be found during the day under stones, logs or among the debris of a roadside dump. Because they like to hide under objects on the ground, a strip of tar paper laid in an open field will attract crickets between late spring and fall. To catch them a collector must turn the tar paper over suddenly and grab them or scoop them into a net.

Newly hatched field crickets eat grass and clover seeds, but in a day or two they relish the same type of food as that prescribed for cockroaches. They are especially fond of fresh lettuce, bits of apple, moistened bran, and dog biscuits. They enjoy drinking drops of water from foliage or from the sides of a screen cage. Camel crickets, hunched-back and wingless, thrive under similar circumstances, but being unable to chirp they have less appeal.

The shiny black beetle, *Passalus cornutus,* can often be found inside soggy hardwood logs. It is about the size of a man's thumb, with a small hook bent forward on top of the head. It is one of the few species of beetles that are both gregarious and can make a noise. The noise is a squeaky sound produced by rubbing hard areas on the upper surface of the abdomen against the lower surface of the corrugated wing covers. It is presumed to help in keeping the adults and grubs from wandering astray down in the dark interior of the log.

But a group of these creatures can be displayed out in the open without too much difficulty. Instead of giving them a log in which to hide, one can give them a shallow layer of sawdust in an advanced stage of decay. The sawdust should be kept moist, and the beetles will not be unduly disturbed by subdued, artificial light. If the sawdust is placed in a shallow pan, then covered with a sheet of glass, moisture will be preserved. The beetles seem to obtain sufficient nourishment from the soggy sawdust to sustain life, and when the grubs come in the spring their parents help break up the larger particles for them. It is best to place a piece of cardboard over the glass when the specimens are not being observed. Frequent removal of refuse will prevent the under surface of the glass from being dirtied.

Insects in Dry Cages

Most insects do best in a dry-bottom cage with a small-necked bottle for water, with a cotton wick as humidifier. If a live plant is in the cage, the humidifier is unnecessary; but the plant should be sprinkled lightly with water each day as a thirst quencher. Food for sucking insects may be supplied by filling a shallow container with a five percent solution of dextrose and then screening the top so that the insects can not tumble in, or by dipping a bunch of flowers in maple or brown sugar syrup thinned with water.

Foliage-eating insects such as caterpillars, sawfly larvae, and some beetle grubs should be provided with fresh leaves every one or two days to keep healthy. Not any kind of leaves will do, but only the particular kind upon which

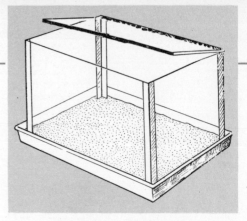

Dry-bottom insect cage

they are known or found to feed. If it happens that a chewing insect is collected without noting its food plant, single leaves from many different plants may be placed in the cage until one leaf is found to be attractive. Many larval insects are specialists and would starve rather than try to survive on an unfamiliar diet.

Bagworms, *Thyridopteryx ephemeraeformis*, can be raised in the early spring simply by breaking off the twigs from which they dangle and stringing them on a thread within a screen cage. There they should be sprinkled from time to time to prevent their drying. Only well-rounded bags are filled with eggs; and since the caterpillars cannot live without food, it is best not to harvest the bags until the leaf buds start to swell. The hatched caterpillars are most interesting to watch as they gorge themselves upon the leaves of hawthorn, locust, and other deciduous and evergreen plants, constructing silk-and-leaf-bags about themselves as they develop.

The egg mass of a praying mantis will hatch readily in a warm, humid room. The young can be fed even in winter upon fruit flies. The weed stems to which the masses are often attached may be stuck upright in the soil of a covered flowerpot or stood erect inside a closed bottle. When the youngsters first hatch they form a rope by clinging to each other's legs, but soon they break their hold and scatter. If not given other food, the strong will eat the weak until only one survives.

During their early youth, praying mantises thrive on a diet of plant lice or fruit flies, but later they eat houseflies, moths, and caterpillars. Their alert front legs and expressive heads rank them first among popular exhibits.

A live colony of ants is always an attraction, provided it is kept under restraint. It lends itself readily to behavioristic studies. Perhaps the easiest to get and maintain are the black pavement ants, *Tetramorium caespitum,* which infest lawns, nest under stones, and raid pantries. They are not more than half an inch long, but very persistent.

They can be displayed in a simple nest made by placing one glass baking dish inside a larger one, filling the space between with water to form a moat about three inches across. It is helpful to divide the smaller dish with plasticine or similar material into four rooms; a food room, nursery, royal chamber, and morgue. One corner of the dish should be walled off for a pool. Keep the nursery dark, covered with an opaque lid, except once or twice a day when it is being examined. A sheet of glass had best be placed over the entire

A cricket cage

small dish to prevent ants from drowning or attempting to cross the moat on floating debris.

Once the partitions are in place, with gaps in the walls to let the ants go from room to room, the covered dish should be taken into the field and placed beside a pavement anthill. A scoopful of soil containing about 50 adult ants, several dozen larvae (like polished rice) and pupae (like wheat grains) should be dug up with a trowel and emptied into the uncovered nursery. The lid should then be clamped on. It would be fine if a queen, whose body is larger than the rest, has been captured; but so long as larvae and pupae are obtained , the queen is generally not essential. She will develop later.

Provided the pool is kept supplied with water, the soil mildly damp, the food room stocked with bits of fatty meat or freshly killed insects, the nursery warm and clean, the colony should thrive. But if by chance the nest has been stocked with sweet-loving ants, they will have to be provided with thin syrup, sugar, or honey in place of meat to keep them alive.

Water Insects

In many respects aquatic insects are the simplest to raise and to display. Of course the aquarium should not be placed in too strong a light, where algae will multiply and spoil the specimens, nor should chemically foul water be used as a culture medium. The center of the aquarium had best be placed at about eye level for observation purposes. But water insects are less susceptible to temperature changes than land insects and are not bothered with problems of relative humidity.

Mosquito wrigglers can be raised in a shallow enamel pan, but a deeper receptacle is better for observing their activity. Students following their development, noting that wrigglers are the forerunners of mosquitoes, are generally impressed with the importance of elimi-

Diving beetles

nating breeding places from their own neighborhood. Wrigglers can be scooped up in a white cup or dipper from almost any stagnant pool during warm weather, and emptied into a quart jar together with the accompanying water. The top of the jar had best be kept covered with a cone made of fly screening to prevent escape of the developed adults.

The wrigglers will thrive for a short time in the water in which they were found; but to keep them alive until they change into pupae they should be fed each day small amounts of finely grated dog biscuits, tiny dried bread crumbs, or dehydrated skimmed milk. They should not be given more than the can readily consume. If a film should form on the surface of the water, the specimens will have to be transferred to a fresh aquarium. Adult house mosquitoes can be kept alive for several weeks by placing freshly soaked or boiled raisins in their cage.

Mosquito wrigglers are food for dragonfly nymphs and waterscorpions. Placed together in the same aquarium, the results are exciting. A ladder of gauze, dangling into the water from the side of the aquarium will furnish an escape for nymphs that are about to change into dragonflies.

Many water scavenger beetles, diving beetles, and predacious and giant water bugs do surprisingly well in an aquarium if a small piece of raw, lean beef is suspended on a hook in the water. It should be removed within 24 hours, however, or pollution will take place. Whirligig beetles and water striders, mainly surface creatures, thrive on small moths and flies tossed alive onto the water.

There are literally thousands of other insects that might be mentioned. But by following the techniques for the various groups reviewed, it is hoped that the task of raising insects will be lightened and that more education by observation will result.

Recommended Reading

The Book of Wild Pets — Clifford B. Moore. Charles T. Branford Co., Boston.

Cultural Methods for Invertebrate Animals — James G. Needham. Comstock Publishing Company, Inc., Ithaca, New York.

Field Book of Insects — Frank E. Lutz, Putnam's Sons, New York.

Field Book of Ponds and Streams — Ann H. Morgan. G.P. Putnam's Sons, New York.

Handbook of Nature Study — Anna B. Comstock, Comstock Publishing Company, Inc., Ithaca, New York

The Insect Guide—Ralph B. Swain. Doubleday &'Co., New York.
Insects in Their World—Written and Illustrated by SuZan N. Swain. Garden City Books, Garden City, New York.

INSECT CONTROL

Insect invasions that strip the leaves off trees are nothing new in North America. But they are new to millions of people who have moved out of urban centers into the suburban countryside.

Thus, when caterpillars denude the woods or fruit trees next door, it becomes a personal matter of immediate concern: Few realize that it is problem as old as the land itself.

In 1795 the first entomological paper by an American was not on a fruit or vegetable insect but the cankerworm, a leaf feeder on deciduous trees. Although cankerworms can defoliate trees, their most annoying habit is spinning down silken threads on to the heads and possessions of the homeowner.

To early New England settlers, 1646 and 1649 were "caterpillar years." In 1797, forest tent caterpillars were "sometimes so plentiful . . . as to strip oak trees bare." This forest insect problem is closely related to changing land use—from the dense forests of pioneer days, to an agricultural economy, to an industrial, urban-centered economy.

In Connecticut, which is typical in many respects of the history of land use in the northeastern United States, the forests were cut until more than two-thirds of the state was cleared for farms. It became unprofitable even in the 19th Century to operate many of these farms, so farmers moved westward or to the cities. Then the forest grew back, until today almost two-thirds of Connecticut is woodland again.

In some areas the forest was cut repeatedly to provide charcoal for the brass and iron industries of the 19th Century. Consequently, only those trees that sprouted vigorously survived—principally oaks and chestnuts.

Thus, the oaks were available to the larvae of the gypsy moth when, in 1869, a French astronomer in Medford, Massachusetts, imported the European insect. He was experimenting with a native American silkworm and possibly wanted to cross the two. A few gypsy moth larvae escaped and, within 20 years, the insects had defoliated some fruit and shade trees in an area of 220 square miles.

They swarmed into the oak forest and, by 1904, had reached the borders of Connecticut. By 1934 they had reached the New York border.

The gypsy moth is aptly named as it travels light, far, and fast. Newly hatched larvae have long hairs that enable them to be carried long distances by the wind. The full-grown caterpillar is brownish-yellow with blue and red dots. It is 1½ to 2½ inches long. The white female moth does not fly. The brown male moth, with some black on the wings has a 1½-inch wingspread. Gypsy moth larvae devour leaves of oaks, birches, poplars, beeches, fruit trees, and even pines, spruces, and hemlocks.

With the coming of the automobile and the move of many people to the suburbs, isolated woodlots became choice homesites. Oaks of poor quality were viewed as prized ornamentals instead of scrub growth. Oak-preying insects, once ignored, now were viewed as pests. The residential woodland was appropriately called "the suburban forest."

In this people-forest-insect relationship the insects are the main unknown factor. Why, for example, did an oakworm infestation suddenly expand from a few acres to 37,000 acres and then fall back to its original level? Why is the oak worm principally found in eastern Connecticut whereas the gypsy moth is more prevalent in western Connecticut? What are the reasons for the periodic outbreaks of the cankerworm? Many studies have been concerned with insect control and much has been learned about the insects' life histories and natural enemies. Now, research is being directed at more fundamental objectives: to find the reasons for the fluctuations of insect populations. This should enable man to predict periods of insect abundance. But, for most insects, this is far in the future. At present the decision to spray or not to spray is little more than an intelligent guess.

When the gypsy moth first became a problem, the United States Department of Agriculture imported many of the insect's natural enemies from abroad in order to combat it. These efforts were so successful that in Connecticut the gypsy moth is now considered to have reached the status of a "naturalized" insect. Like native insects its populations fluctuate. Years of caterpillar abundance are followed by years of scarcity.

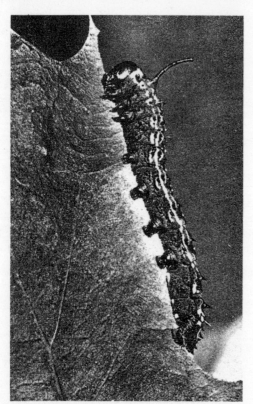

Orange-striped oak worm

The reasons for the cyclic nature of these insect outbreaks are very poorly understood, but undoubtedly predators, parasites, weather, disease, genetics, and physiology all play a part.

Unfortunately, natural controls do not always reduce a population of forest insects as much, or as quickly, as a homeowner might wish. There is usually a lag before predators and parasites can noticeably reduce the numbers of their host.

Though insecticides are usually thought of first for quick results, other avenues are also being explored to avoid the use of insecticides on forests. Such possibilities as sterility techniques, attractants, repellents, more specific insecticides, and diseases are being studied.

Before we condemn those wishing to spray, however, we should observe an area of heavy caterpillar infestation. The numbers of caterpillars are almost unbelievable. They fall from the trees, crawl over the sidewalks, creep in the windows; they are crushed under foot and their droppings leave stains on clothes and houses.

Twice in the space of a few years in Connecticut it was necessary to sand roads in midsummer because the crushed oak worms made the roads too slippery for safety. Fortunately such occurrences are not common.

Such infestations by the orange-striped oak worm were so common in 1957 and 1958 that some citizens pressed for a statewide program of insecticidal sprays. On biological evidence and past history this did not seem advisable and the area of defoliation decreased naturally from 37,000 acres in 1958 to about 20 acres in 1960.

This is probably not evidence against *all* spraying, however, as each case must be decided separately. Drawing direct analogies between different situations is as dangerous in biology as elsewhere.

As our modes of living change, so do the insects that bother the householder.

Insects that live in fireplace logs emerge in the house to annoy the owner. These insects, harmless in themselves, are of grave concern to the owner who does not know where they came from or on what they feed.

Structural pests in wood are, of course, all too prevalent in many areas, but insects such as carpenter ants and termites that live in wood may be of vital concern to the homeowner in the suburban woodland.

In addition to the insects that feed on trees, the suburban landowner even more often meets insects that annoy him. Mosquitoes, blackflies, and punkies emerge from the stream or pond that made the area so attractive to the home buyer. Mosquito control programs, which were conceived to reduce the incidence of malaria and other insect-borne diseases, sometimes become programs to insure that no one gets bitten. This was especially true after the introduction of DDT.

This, of course, is a legitimate objective if a person understands that that is what he is paying for. In the suburban forest, however, insect control is often a matter of esthetics rather than necessity.

Moreover, the pattern of country living has changed. The farmer cleared his acres of trees for some distance about his house, whereas the suburbanite often chooses to place his house in the woods. He is thus more vulnerable to the ravages of forest insects, which can build up to surprising numbers very quickly.

In cases of bad infestations, an individual cannot protect himself with insecticides if his neighbors do not do likewise. Some migrating larvae can crawl surprising distances.

The ultimate decision on how the relationship between forests, insects, and people will be adjusted rests primarily on man. Each person must decide what things are most important and should understand the biological implications of his decision. In Connecticut, for example, the final decision to spray for gypsy moth control rests with the individual towns.

Some of the factors that should be weighed in the decision are listed in the accompanying table. In the table, complete defoliation or spraying are considered as the only alternatives, but usually it is not so clear-cut a decision.

It has been stated that the cost of controlling the gypsy moth in Connecticut probably only equals the value of the timber saved. If this estimate is correct, then the gypsy moth control program can be justified only on esthetic grounds.

Farther west in New York State it is justified on the basis of preventing the spread of the gypsy moth westward. In New York, blanket sprays cover large areas; in Connecticut the sprayed areas are carefully limited to areas of worst infestation. Whether either or both of these types of spraying is truly justified depends on an individual's point of view. Certainly, with present insecticides and techniques of application it is extremely improbable that the gypsy moth can be eradicated from the Northeast

Research with the recently developed synthetic male attractant, or experiments with irradiated pupae may lead in the near future to some new means of eradication.

There is nothing inherently wrong in man s efforts to modify the environment, any more than it is wrong for the forest tent caterpillar to "strip the oak trees bare." Man has the opportunity, however, to choose his course of action and to foresee the probable results. If he does not wish to modify his environment more than he has done, then he must be willing to accept the pains as well as the pleasures of life in the suburban forest.   —S.W.H.

Insect Distribution

Every species of animal or plant survives under certain conditions of temperature, moisture, light, available food, and other elements that influence or control its distribution. The required conditions are somewhat different for every species. If several—or often, only one—of the factors favorable to it are lacking, the species concerned may not be able to exist within a region.

For example, orchids do not grow in deserts because they need moisture, although there are places in a desert where all their other living requirements are present. A case more to the point is that of the four-spotted anopheles mosquito, *Anopheles quadrimaculatus,* of the southern United States. The insect is never found very far north of the latitude of Columbus, Ohio; the accepted reason is that the larval mosquito, or wriggler, cannot survive for long—or at least it does not develop—in water of a temperature below 70° F. A related species, *Anopheles punctipennis,* since it *can* endure colder water, lives farther north.

The factors that limit the distribution of an animal are not always clear. This is especially true of the falcate orange-tip butterfly, *Euchloe genutia.* The geographic distribution of this creature is supposed to include all of the United States east of the Rocky Mountains, yet people find the insect only in limited areas. It has been collected in every state south of Lake Michigan and east of the Mississippi River, but always at widely separated places. No one seems to have a reasonable explanation for this spotty distribution of *Euchloe.* Although it is often considered alpine (a species inhabiting mountain summits and cool, northern regions) it is found at low altitudes in Arkansas in hot weather. Food may have something to do with the matter, yet this is difficult to understand because the caterpillar, or larval form, feeds on a wide variety of cresses and mustards.

The case of the falcate orange-tip butterfly illustrates, incidentally, that localized animal populations do not necessarily indicate rarity. This butterfly is certainly not rare; its numbers are simply concentrated in limited areas within its wide range.

Some animals are so selective about their food that their distribution is restricted to where their favored food plant grows, but this is true of only a very few insects. The Chinese silkworm, to be sure, thrives only upon leaves of the white mulberry, but this is also unique among insects. Even plant-feeding species are usually capable of living on several different kinds of plants, although some tend to feed upon one species where it is common. Such a case is that of the pestiferous Colorado potato beetle, which eats potato plants and causes great damage to them where they are grown in great numbers. It will also feed on tomatoes, eggplant, and in fact on almost any member of the nightshade family to which the potato belongs. Some carnivorous insects are selective in their food habits, but many are not. And there are insects—ants, for example—that will eat both plants and animals.

The particular locality in which an insect is found may be the result of its habits, and these in turn may depend upon the physical limitations of the animal itself. The blackwing damselfly is never found flying over large, open bodies of water, but is confined to woodland pools or small streams that meander through willows. The blackwing is not a strong flier; in the open it would be exposed to many enemies. It probably feels safe instinctively only in the shaded recesses of the woods. Similarly, certain caddisfly larvae, which make protective cases of small stones, are found, as would be expected, only in brooks with sandy bottoms.

The local distribution or habitat of an adult insect also may be somewhat different from that of its young. Although the caterpillars of the mourning cloak butterfly are often found on willows in open marshes, the butterfly itself is seldom seen there. Evidently the female only stops long enough to lay her eggs, and the emerging butterflies do not linger long in the marshland. The adult mourning cloak is a creature of lawns, parks, and open woodlands, where it flutters slowly between trees or rests upon a sunny place on the forest floor. The fact remains that the female mourning cloak butterfly, although she may visit a marsh to lay eggs, does not, like the fritillary butterflies, revel in hot, open, sunny places.

A person without experience in collecting insects in a given area is often astonished at the number of curious, unfamiliar ones in a private or public collection. But if he himself begins to collect in the same area, he is equally astonished to find how many insects, once unknown to him, are relatively common. This is because he gradually learns where and when to look for species that he has reason to suspect are present. Yet even the experienced collector is sometimes deceived. (*See also Insect Rarity*) —C.E.A.

Insect Gallmakers

Students of natural history who go to the woods and fields for first-hand knowledge of plants and animals are certain to see many abnormal growths on the leaves and stems of a great variety of plants. These growths, known as galls (*See Gall*), are generally caused by insects. They vary greatly in form, size, and color and may be found at any time of the year. Some are like fruits in shape and coloring; some are fragile and easily crushed; others are so hard and woody that a sharp knife is needed to cut them.

Each of the different kinds of insect galls is produced by a certain insect that attacks a particular part of a particular plant. There are hundreds of species of gall-producing insects. These little creatures make their plant-host provide both food and shelter for their young. They lay their eggs on leaves or stems or roots, and the plant tissues grow out around

Witch-hazel gall

Pinecone willow gall

Oak bullet gall

the developing larva to form the gall.

Most galls are simple, developing around a single insect larva; a few are multiple, resulting when a number of eggs have been deposited close together. If a growing gall is opened carefully, the insect tenant will be found in a snug larval chamber in the center. Most species of gall-making insects complete their development within the gall, the adults tunneling their way out when they reach maturity. A few leave the gall as full-fed larvae, completing development outside

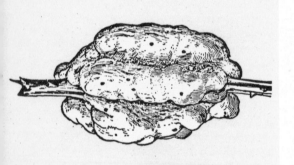

Blackberry knot gall

The white-footed mouse feeds on the insect larve concealed within certain galls

the gall. The little round holes to be seen on old, dry galls are the exits through which the insects escaped.

For many centuries galls have been known and studied by man. The great Italian physician, Malpighi, was the first to write a systematic account of galls. In 1686 he published a very accurate description of the galls then found in Italy and Sicily. Malpighi observed that the formation of the gall followed the puncture of the plant tissue by the insect, and it was his theory that the insect injected some substance into the plant that stimulated the abnormal growth.

Some galls are useful. One kind was used by the Greeks as a fuel in lamps; some are used as food and medicine. Certain oak galls are important in the making of ink, and others in tanning and dying skins and wool. On the other hand, many galls are harmful. For instance, there are those caused by the Hessian fly midge that may destroy large areas of wheat, or those of the clover midge that make it impossible to grow the seeds of clover in certain areas. In addition there is, of course, the damage done to many useful and beautiful plants. (*For insect parasites see under Beetle; and under this heading: Insect Predators; and Insect Values*)

Recommended Reading

Field Book of Insects—Frank E. Lutz. G. P. Putnam's Sons, New York.
Insect Transmission of Plant Disease—Julian G. Leach. McGraw-Hill, New York.
Insects and Plants—Irving and Ruth Adler. John Day Company, New York.
Insects in Relation to Plant Diseases—W. Carter. John Wiley and Sons (Interscience), New York.
Key to American Insect Galls—Ephraim P. Felt. New York State Museum Bulletin.
Plant Galls and Gall Makers—Ephraim P. Felt. Comstock Publishing Company, Ithaca, New York.
Plants, Viruses, and Insects—Katherine Esau. Harvard University Press, Cambridge, Massachusetts.

Insects of Ponds and Streams

When the ice has melted in ponds and along the edges of woodland streams, people often feel the urge to go collecting in the country. There is no more stimulating and interesting expedition than an early spring insect-collecting trip to a pond teeming with reawakened life. The serious collector should have a net or a long-handled wire sieve, a white enamel pan, a pair of small pincers, and a few wide-mouthed bottles in which to take away specimens. The pincers will be useful for handling the insects that have piercing mouth parts. An extra pair of dry shoes and stockings will be useful for the trip home.

Water insects do not live far from shore and some species can be scooped off the surface of the water, others out of the mud and leaves on the bottom, and still others off the water plants among which many species hide. On a single trip, even an amateur collector can find many of the common forms and can observe their behavior and adaptations to life in the water.

Since most water insects are carnivorous and feed voraciously on one another, the contents of each scoopful should be sorted as it is emptied into the white enamel pan. Place a little sand in the bottom of each jar, include a branch or two of water plant, and add water from the pond before including the insects.

The day's catch should provide a person with sufficient material for several weeks, or even months, of observation and entertainment. Water insects make excellent pets and can be kept in a simple aquarium. Jelly glasses, fruit jars, and other clear glass dishes can be used, as well as more expensive tanks.

Some Common Water Insects

All aquatic insects have the typical insect form and go through the same changes during their life histories as their land relatives. The adults have

Ponds teem with insect life

six legs and an outside skeleton of chitinous, or horny, material. Practically all adult aquatic insects breathe air; many of them fly far from water and return only to lay their eggs.

1. Dragonflies and Damselflies (Odonata). Very common near ponds and streams, dragonflies and damselflies are perhaps the best known of water insects, although only the larvae are aquatic. Adult dragonflies, sometimes called devil's darning needles, have four strong, net-veined, transparent wings, which are extended out from their sides when the dragonflies are at rest. Damselflies are smaller and more delicately built and, when at rest, their wings are held vertically over their backs. Both dragonflies and damselflies feed on insects caught in flight, the hairy legs acting as basketlike traps. The larvae, or nymphs, are aquatic and carnivorous, eating many other water insects. The nymph possesses an elongated and hinged lower lip, ending in efficient pincers for catching prey. When not in

use the lip is folded backward under the head. Damselfly larvae are slender nymphs and may be identified by the three leaflike gills at the end of the abdomen. The female dragonfly lays her eggs as she skims over the water, dipping the tip of her abdomen beneath the surface. Damselflies place their eggs within the leaves and stems of water plants.

2. Water bugs (Hemiptera). Water bugs live in still pools along quiet streams or the protected, weedy shores of ponds and lakes. There they are found in great numbers from early spring until late autumn, foraging among water plants and decaying vegetation. One common species, the water strider, lives on the surface film. The majority of the water bugs are predacious and all have sharp, sucking beaks. All must come to the surface for air and all have incomplete metamorphosis—that is, the young look and act like adults. In this group are the oval, flattened giant water bugs, ogres lurking in the mud; the little backswimmers and water boatmen, with their oarlike hind legs; the sluggish waterscorpions, characterized, by the long, respiratory tail; and the water striders, skating on the surface film.

3. Mayflies (Ephemeroptera). As winged adults, the mayflies live only a few hours, or days at the most, but life in the water as a nymph may last for as much as three years. Adult mayflies are beautiful, fragile insects with four delicate wings—two large front ones and two small hind one—and two or three slender tail filaments. The nymphs are found in clean water and live entirely on plant food. They are, therefore, easily kept in an aquarium stocked with algae and water plants.

4. Caddis flies (Trichoptera). Adult caddis flies look like moths and are probably related to the ancestors of butterflies and moths. The aquatic larvae are interesting creatures, known

The water strider lives on the surface film of ponds

as caddis worms. They construct about themselves elaborate tubes of sticks, bits of leaves, and grains of sand, which are fastened together with silk. Caddis worms move about in the water with heads and legs sticking out of their little self-made homes. Most caddis worms are thought to be vegetarians. They are excellent aquarium pets and many interesting experiments can be carried out with them.

5. Water beetles (Coleoptera). The majority of the beetles are land insects but a few are aquatic. They have complete metamorphosis and the larvae in no way resemble the adults. Most aquatic beetles live in quiet water and, therefore, thrive in aquariums, where their swimming, feeding, and breathing habits can be studied. Some are vegetable eaters but the majority are predacious. The whirligig beetles, gyrating on the surface of quiet water, are very common and easily recognized. Other forms, certain to be collected from the bottom vegetation of most ponds, are the brownish crawling water beetles and the bloodthirsty, predacious diving beetles, the Dytiscidae, with their fierce larvae, called water tigers.

6. Mosquitoes (Diptera). Several species of two-winged flies have aquatic larvae. They include gnats, midges, punkies, crane flies and mosquitoes. The larvae of mosquitoes are called wrigglers and they are to be found in almost any standing bodies of water—lakes, ponds, puddles, and rain barrels. Since they all breathe air and must come to the surface for fresh supplies, a film of oil on the surface of the water smothers the wrigglers. However, control of mosquitoes can be accomplished best by draining swamps and useless pools, and keeping lakes and ponds stocked with fish, which eat the larvae. (*See also under Pond: Animal Life in a Pond*)

Recommended Reading

Caddis-fly Larvae as Masons and Builders— Frank E. Lutz. Museum of Natural History, New York.

Field Book of Ponds and Streams—Ann Morgan. C. P. Putnam's Sons, New York.

1001 Questions Answered About Insects— Alexander B. and Elsie B. Klots. Dodd, Mead & Company, New York.

Insect Predators

Man, used to conflicts and struggles, many of which are of his own making is familiar with war. Sometimes, too, it seems that all the forces of nature are fighting against him. Yet this is not so, for there is one struggle going on about him that works eternally for his benefit.

It is a conflict that takes place in the air above, in the ground below, and in the fields and streams. It is the natural preying of one insect on another, and because of the astounding numbers of the participants, it is one that is fraught with potential danger if man interferes too much or too often.

Although many people do not appreciate it, most insects are beneficial to man and they are vitally necessary to all other forms of life on this planet. Nearly a million species of insects have already been classified. Some serve as food for fishes, game, and fowl, and

without insects many animals would starve. Some pollinate plants, and without insects these plants could not survive. Some carry germs of decay or eat at rubble to clear away the endless filth, debris, and fallen bodies that, without insects, would soon encompass the earth. Some in their very destruction of plantlife, hold undesirable weeds in check. And some help to check the numbers of other insects by acting as natural predators. Without insects, life would soon perish from the earth.

In her book, *Insect Fact and Folklore,* Lucy W. Clausen gives an estimate of one year's possible volume from a single pair of houseflies. From spring until fall, the total number would reach 191,010,000,000,000,000,000. That quintillion figure includes the multiplication by offspring. A single fly mother would produce a total of only 1,950 eggs, but she is a small producer when compared with a termite queen. The queen termite can spawn a colony of three million individuals. By actual count, one queen laid 7,000 eggs in one day. When another queen was dissected , 48,000 budding eggs were found in her ovaries at the moment of her death.

Gardeners are familiar with aphids, or plant lice. These miniature creatures are scarcely one-eighth of an inch long and are seemingly weightless. Aphids are found in what appear to be large numbers; but no matter how large the infestation seems to be, it is but the slightest fragment of what could be found under perfect reproduction conditions, and where no enemies to check them were on hand.

The female aphid can give birth to living young without the aid or benefit of a male. This is birth by parathenogenesis. In the spring a female starts to bear living young. Each is a wingless female, which also gives birth to living young. In some species a female starts the reproduction process even before her own birth—so third generations are often on their way before the second generation is born.

These wingless females almost explode into existence, in fantastic numbers. When they threaten to overrun a single plant and when the sap supply suddenly becomes scarce, they all start giving birth to winged females. These winged females fly to new plants, where the procession continues to multiply. In the fall, and by some means that entomologists are unable to explain, males are suddenly born along with the females. Although the female can give birth to living young, she cannot reproduce eggs without fertilization from the male. Only eggs can survive the winter.

Variations in the weather help to control insects. The available food supply, or lack of it, is a determining factor. Fishes, mammals, and birds are all active predators, but the job of insect control is a job done mainly by warring insects. Nature seems to use mammoth numbers to fight mammoth numbers.

Many foes devour the highly prolific aphids. The ladybird beetle, or ladybug, is a chief control of aphids—both in the gaudy red-and-black larval state and as a tough-shelled adult. These little beetles devour aphids by the billions, and they are collected in baskets and sacks and sold commercially for that purpose. It was their value in aphid control that gave birth to their name. Italian farmers in the Middle Ages recognized their important function. So grateful were

the farmers that they dedicated this valuable beetle to the Virgin Mary. The predator became known as *The Beetle of Our Lady*. The names "lady beetle" and "ladybug" naturally followed.

It is an unusual piece of property that does not have several anthills. An anthill may be the home of 500,000 ants. The ant is a constant threat to termites. As the official of a termite-control company once noted, "No one will ever eliminate termites. The best you can do is control them." He told housewives they should be grateful that ant hordes were around to fight the damaging termites.

The tiny ant is also a check on another insect—the praying mantis, which is not always economically valuable in its eating habits. Mantises eat useful as well as destructive insects. Ants eat mantis egg sacs (each sac contains about 200 eggs) and ants are about the only insect the large mantis seems to fear. A mantis that can kill a black widow spider with ease will squirm quickly away from the tiniest ant.

Ants have enemies, too—among them the buried ant-lion, a larval insect that waits at the bottom of a conical sand-pit it has dug which traps ants and other insects.

Most insects play a helpful role at some time or other. Even the termite is helpful in destroying old wood in

Lady beetle

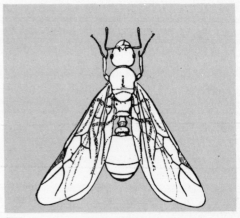

Ant

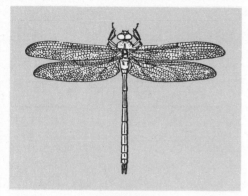

Dragonfly

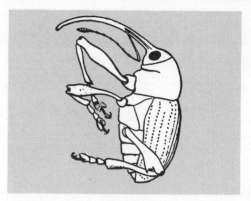

Weevil

forests—a task that is necessary to the natural functioning of ecological changes in a woodland.

Dragonflies live as voracious nymphs before emerging as winged fliers. These nymphs propel themselves through the water by exuding water from their bodies from which the oxygen has been extracted. They have jaws fastened on a pair of long, armlike appendages and each nymph takes a large toll of mosquito larvae. When dragonflies emerge as adults, they are colorful, swift-flying creatures. They have as many as 30,000 separate lenses in each compound eye, and their eyesight is superior to that of most insects—equaled in sharpness, perhaps, only by that of the swift-flying robber fly.

Dragonfly numbers can be enormous. Driving down a central Kansas road in the summer of 1952, some observers saw a vast dragonfly migration that was apparently heading for a feeding mecca in the Ozarks. Driving parallel with them, they clocked the dragonflies at slightly over 40 miles per hour. They were in formation, about one for every cubic yard of air space. The formations could be counted upward to 20 levels, and while they stretched above that, it was impossible to determine how far. The streaming army was 7½ miles wide and it flew forward, unbroken, for 3½ hours. By the most conservative estimate, there were 37 trillion individual

insects. The total number of mosquito larvae that these migrants might have devoured is awe-inspiring—and beyond human comprehension.

Among the 350,000 different kinds of beetles, there are about 20,000 different species of snout beetles. Each snout beetle attacks a different host plant. Most infamous of the tribe is the cotton boll weevil—and the more cotton plants that abound, the more weevils feed on it. Other snout beetles, however, attack weeds and undesirable plants. There is a snout beetle that feeds on ragweed, and so on, each helping to keep one plant from overrunning other plants. Some aphids attack only apple trees, while others feed only on cabbage plants.

If certain insects are specialists in plant consumption, so are some of the predators specialists in insect destruction. A wasp thriving only on apple aphids will bypass thousands of cabbage aphids.

The grubs, or larvae, of blister beetles hunt underground. They seek out the egg masses left by grasshoppers and thus destroy many baby hoppers before they are born. The zooming robber fly, on the other hand, attacks prey only in flight. This swift-flying insect looks like an inch-long version of Lindbergh's *Spirit of St. Louis,* and early airplane designers actually studied the robber fly as a model for airplanes. Armed with a sharp stilettolike beak, the robber fly snatches grasshoppers, moths, houseflies, bumble-bees, and other insects out of the air. The stiletto is driven home, and a paralyzing fluid is injected into the victim by the robber fly, which then alights with its prey and drains it of its body juices. Spiders, although they are not insects, are predators that feed on virtually every type of insect. Some use web snares, others depend upon speed afoot. Just as a robber fly can handle a grasshopper three times its size, so a tiny spider can handle a robber fly with ease. The spider, in turn, falls quick prey to certain wasps.

The tachinid flies scatter thousands of tiny black eggs among grass stems. Crawling caterpillars eat them in passing, only to have the eggs hatch inside their bodies like so many time bombs. The tachina, which looks like another kind of housefly to most people, is such a valuable parasite that entomologists hesitate to evaluate its true worth. The 1,400 different species find hosts among moths, butterflies, beetles, grasshoppers, wasps, earwigs, and crane flies. Foreign species have been imported to help control gypsy moths, brown-tail moths, and Japanese beetles.

Of all the warriors in this deadly game of one insect preying on another, the wasp family may be the most valuable family of all. Although adult wasps feed almost entirely on flower nectar, they capture billions of live insects to feed to their young larvae. Some species chew their prey and pass it on to the babies. Others sting and paralyze their victims, then lay an egg on the immo-bile, but live body. When the egg hatches, the larval wasp has a store of live food to eat. Caterpillars, wood bor-ers, spiders, cicadas, crickets, plant lice, and brown mites are included in the prey. Some are taken to paper houses built by the wasps, some sealed in mud dens, some buried in underground nests, some stung in their own homes inside tree trunks.

Just as a robber fly has a stiletto in

Thin-waisted wasp

the beak, the wasp has a sharp dagger in the tail. A venom, primarily formic acid, is injected along with the sting. Wasp venom is far more powerful than DDT. The Connecticut Agricultural Ex-periment Statio found that one micro-scopic-sized droplet of wasp venom was sufficient to kill 1,600 caterpillars. Ac-cording to Ira La Rivers, wasps kill a million Mormon crickets per square mile per season. Without wasps, these crop-devouring Mormon crickets could over-whelm the earth.

The oriental fruit moth is a serious threat to fruit crops such as peach, apricot, and plum. Insecticidal sprays are ineffective because the larvae feed inside the twigs, so wasp predators are bred and sold to war on the caterpillars of the fruit moth. California insectaries at Riverside and Berkeley incubate and distribute millions of wasps a year. They are sent out in paper bags, 2,500 at a time. Along the East Coast, braconid wasps control 80 percent of the oriental fruit moths.

Because most people notice insects only during large infestations, and be-cause the general public fears almost every insect except butterflies, Ameri-cans have been quick to accept chemical insecticides. Householders spray insects that plague them without knowledge or appreciation of the billions that have been destroyed by natural enemies. Many entomologists warn that the overuse of chemical insecticides poses a great potential danger. House and garden spraying are all right, and so is the elimination of certain breeding areas of certain so-called pest insects, but poison that kills by thousands may eliminate active insect allies that kill by billions.

—J.R.C.

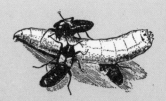

Aleochara bimaculata, *the rove beetle, is a ruthless predator that hunts singly or in small groups. It is the main enemy of the cabbage maggot and preys on a variety of fly larvae*

Lysiphelebus testaceipes, *a small, slender insect, lays its eggs in the body of aphids. The aphid shows no ill effects for about three days but then stops reproducing. Soon after, the rapidly developing larva devours the vital organs of the aphid causing its death*

Pyrgota flies deposit their eggs only in the bodies of May beetles while in flight. In 4 or 5 days the egg hatches and the hungry larva feeds on the body fluids and internal organs of its host. In 10 to 14 days the beetle is dead. In years when May beetles are scarce, pyrgota flies are greatly reduced in numbers

Trichogramma minutum, *an egg parasite, places its eggs in the eggs of moths. It is extremely beneficial, because it destroys many of the insects most injurious to crops. Research is being conducted on the use of these parasites as pest control agents*

Many insects are attacked and killed by other insects either for food or as a place to deposit their eggs, in which case the host is destroyed by the developing larva. Insect parasites are of great importance to man in keeping down the number of insects, many of which are injurious to food crops

The royal walnut moth

Insect Rarity

Not all kinds of insects are equally common. Some, indeed, are so rare that even the serious collector is fortunate if he finds them once in his lifetime. True, a relatively common species may seem rare simply because an individual does not know where to look for it, but when a trained observer fails to find it, it is certainly not a common species. When numerous naturalists, combing the country for insects, find that a species has been found only occasionally, that species may, indeed, be considered rare.

The royal walnut moth, *Citheronia regalis*, for example, is widely distributed in the United States east of the Rocky Mountains, from the Gulf of Mexico to Labrador. The caterpillar, or larval form of this moth, feeds chiefly upon the leaves of hickory trees, which are certainly not uncommon plants. The caterpillar, known as the hickory horned devil, does not get competition from other insects, since those that do feed on hickory are seldom found in large numbers. Yet despite all this, it is a fortunate person who ever sees either the adult royal walnut moth or its caterpillar. Nowhere in the region that it inhabits is this insect found in great numbers. In nearly 50 years of collecting and studying insects, one entomologist saw only one adult living specimen and one caterpillar.

The royal walnut moth is a handsome creature with a wingspread of four or five inches. The fore wings are steel blue with red veins; the hind wings are a soft brown. There are large patches of yellow irregularly distributed on all of the wings. The sexes are quite similar, excepting that the male is somewhat smaller than the female and is usually darker. The caterpillar is quite as conspicuous as the moth itself, for in addition to being four or five inches in length and as thick as a man s thumb, it bears on the upper forepart of its body several pairs of curved horns, which give it its common name. Despite its fearsome appearance it is quite harmless.

Rarity is not, however, invariably associated with large size and striking appearance. In proof of this there is *Merope tuber*, a relative of the scorpion flies, a creature at once so rare and so inconspicuous that it has no common English name. It is nondescript in color; it is small with a wingspread of about one inch and it is without any peculiarity except that the male bears at the "tail" end of his body a pair of "forceps." *Merope tuber* has the singular distinction of being the only representative of its genus and its family, Meropidae, in the United States. Its life history is unknown. Presumably, the immature insect resembles a caterpillar, for this creature belongs to the order Mecoptera to which the scorpion flies belong, and the young scorpion fly is very much like a caterpillar.

None of the Mecoptera are very common. One collector of insects has come

The caterpiller of the royal walnut moth is called the hickory horned devil

The black dragonfly is considered a rare species although it is not as uncommon as some others

upon little groups of adult scorpion flies twice in his life, and both times the species were different. Yet all scorpion flies are very much alike. Their wings, similar in size and shape, are straw-colored with brown blotches, giving them a rather attractive appearance. The males are remarkable in that the "tail," really the abdomen, is narrowed and then enlarged at the end to form a bulbous part armed with a pair of "pincers." Thus the body of the creature does bear a singular resemblance to the scorpion, to which it is in no way related; nor is it a fly.

The black dragon, *Hagenius brevistylus,* is a large dragonfly with colorless wings and a body beautifully marked with white streaks and spots. Although technically it is one of the club-tails, it differs so markedly from all other dragonflies that it is not likely to be mistaken for any of them.

While the black dragon is not as uncommon as some other insects, seldom will more than one or two be found in one place at one time. This is remarkable when one considers that there is scarcely another species of dragonfly in our country that does not occasionally appear in enormous numbers.

In the past so much publicity has been given to the royal walnut moth that some people believe that it is the only moth that is rare. Yet another equally conspicuous rare moth is the fireweed hawkmoth, *Celerio intermedia.* This belongs to that group of moths that have elongated, vibrating wings and are sometimes mistaken for hummingbirds. The fireweed hawkmoth must be very rare. Few collectors have ever seen one alive. The strangest thing about this insect's rarity is that the closely related lined hawkmoth, *Celerio lineata,* is very common indeed. One could easily collect a dozen specimens of the lined hawkmoth in an hour at a petunia bed.

Certainly the fireweed hawkmoth is not overlooked by entomologists. It has a wingspread of at least three inches with a conspicuous pattern of pink and black. Nor can its rarity be blamed on a lack of proper food, since fireweed, *Epilobium angustifolium,* upon which the caterpillar feeds, is a very common plant occurring throughout the eastern United States and in Kansas, Arizona, and California.

Perhaps the most interesting of all rare insects is the *Mantispa.* The name represents several species but all are rare and all are pretty much alike in appearance and habits. *Mantispa* has no common name. It is sometimes mistaken for the praying mantis, which it remarkably resembles, although the lat-

The fireweed hawkmoth is very rare even though fireweed, on which it feeds, is a widely distributed species

Mantispa is often mistaken for the praying mantis

ter insect has a different set of ancestors, being related to the grasshoppers, while *Mantispa* is cousin to the dobsonfly of which hellgrammites, the larval form, are a well-known fish bait.

One finds here a remarkable example of what naturalists call *ecological convergence*—that is, the fact that two animals with different ancestors have come to resemble each other because of similarities in their methods of living. Both lie in wait for prey, which they seize with their powerful forelegs. There are a number of distinct differences, nevertheless, between praying mantises and mantispids. All mantispids are small, averaging less than an inch in length. Mantises, although some are small, vary greatly in size. The big Chinese mantis, *Paratenodera sinensis*, which has been established in the United States, is four or five inches long. The wings of the mantispids are of the lace-winged type found in dobsons and dragonflies, whereas the wings of the mantises are of the grasshopper type.

Finally, the development of the two insects differs. The mantispids have a complete metamorphosis in which the young insect is unlike the adult in appearance and passes through a sleeping, or pupa, stage, before becoming adult. At hatching, the young mantis resembles the adult except that it is smaller and

has no wings, and it remains active throughout life. The mantispids are active hunters only as adults, and the female lays her eggs upon spider or insect eggs, which her emerging progeny devour. The small size of mantispids may partly explain why they are not found more frequently, yet it seems probable that they are relatively rare.

No one knows for certain why some insects are rarer than others. It is difficult to find any one cause of rarity. Scarcity of a particular food suggests itself as a possible cause for the rarity of some insects, but it certainly cannot be true for all of them. Nor does competition for food explain the matter. The caterpillar of the royal walnut moth shares its diet of walnut or hickory leaves with a number of other insects that are not numerous enough, even when all of them are taken together, to seriously injure the trees upon which they feed. Therefore it can scarcely be true that the royal walnut moth is crowded out by other insects. The lined hawkmoth, it is true, has a wider choice of food plants than has the fireweed hawkmoth, yet the food of the fireweed hawkmoth is certainly not in short supply.

Predators and parasites seem to take no more toll of rare species than of commoner kinds. They should, in fact, have less effect, for it is an established natural law that in order for a predator to survive, the creatures upon which it lives must be able to breed much more rapidly than the predator or parasite. It is improbable that rare animals breed very rapidly. Of course, little is known about the predators and parasites of rare animals, because their very rarity makes it difficult to study the problem carefully and in detail. Rarity is more likely to result from low vitality and reproductive rate than from any other factor.

Without doubt some insects are rare because they have passed their historical prime. This may be the case with *Merope tuber*, as well as with the

Mecoptera as a group. Many millions of years ago there existed an order of insects known as Megasecoptera. It has long since become extinct, but in the meantime has given rise to the Diptera, or two-winged flies, and to the Mecoptera. The two-winged flies, of which the mosquito and housefly are examples, are highly specialized, modern insects, very successful in maintaining themselves. The scorpion flies, on the other hand, although they have become specialized in some respects, have for the most part retained ancestral structures and habits that are liabilities today. Perhaps they too will disappear, as have many extinct forms of life that failed to adapt themselves to an everchanging world.(*See also under Insect Distribution*)
—C.E.A.

Insect Sounds

Insects are among the world's oldest soundmakers. While it is true that the great majority of insect species are silent, sounds of different kinds and intensities are produced by a number of species scattered through a few groups of insects. The music is entirely instrumental, as no insect possesses a true voice. Throughout the warmer months the vast insect orchestra plays in woods and fields—a monotonous, insistent rhythm.

In most cases, sound production is confined to the males, although some females possess the same faculty. The significance of the sounds produced is not always known. In many insects the sounds are probably concerned with the attraction of the sexes; in others they seem to communicate some kind of intelligence—such as recognition or danger—to other members of the species. Some entomologists believe that many insect sounds have no biological significance.

In some insects the sounds are produced by vibrations of uncertain origin, but the known methods by which the more common sounds are produced may be classified as follows:

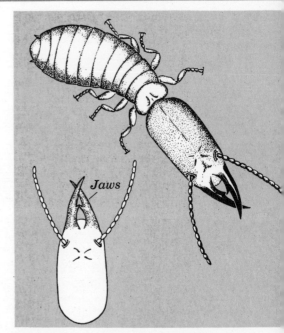

The termite "soldier" makes tapping and clicking sounds by snapping its jaws and knocking its head against solid objects

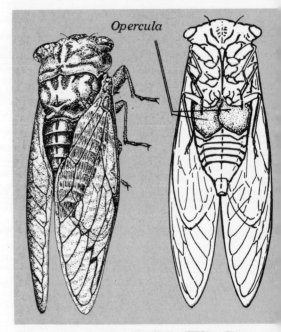

The male cicada has complex sound-producing chambers in its abdomen. The covering plates on these chambers are called opercula

A. By the vibration of the wings. Many insects make a humming or buzzing sound when flying. The wings vibrate with sufficient speed and regularity to give a definite note. Most people familiar with what Emerson called the "mellow, breezy bass" of the bumblebee, as it drones over a flower, and with the higher, busy hum of the worker honeybee, collecting pollen and nectar; some people have heard the dry rustle of the vibrating wings of dragonflies along the borders of ponds and streams— "tilting down the waters in a wild, bewildered flight," as Riley described the dragonfly; and few, if any have escaped the maddening hum of the mosquito's wings as that ubiquitous insect hovers nearby. Other insects, including flies and some beetles, make "music" by this method.

B. By the tapping of some part of the body against an external object. One of the best examples of this method of sound-making is found in beetles of the genus *Anobium*. These beetles burrow into old furniture or woodwork, where they make tapping or ticking sounds that are believed to be sex calls. The sound is made by the insect striking its head against the wood where it burrows.

Among some of the termites (popularly called white ants, but not even closely related to ants) the "soldiers" of the colony can be distinguished from the "workers" by their large broad and hard heads with large powerful jaws. These soldiers knock their heads against the ground or wood of the nest and snap their jaws, making tapping and clicking sounds audible to the human ear. This tapping serves as a signal to the workers when danger threatens the colony. The workers feel the vibrations produced by the tapping and clicking rather than hear them

The male common field cricket makes chirping sounds with his fore wings by moving the right wing rapidly over the left. The sound is produced by the rasping of the scraper of one wing against the file of the other

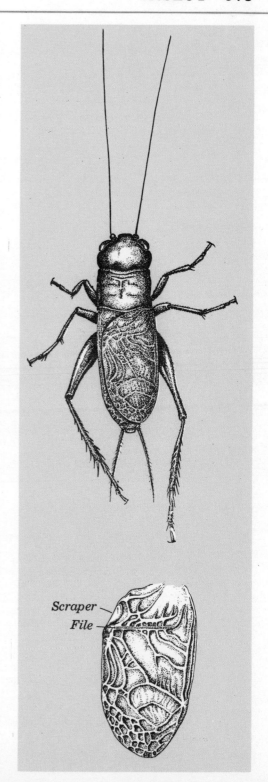

Scraper
File

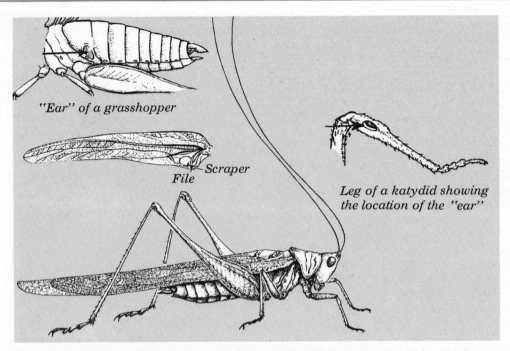

"Ear" of a grasshopper

Scraper
File

Leg of a katydid showing
the location of the "ear"

*The male long-horned grasshopper makes sounds with a scraper and file similar to
that of the common field cricket. Grasshoppers and their relatives are among the
few insects that have true hearing structures*

C. Sounds produced by the vibration of special membranes, controlled by muscular action. The cicadas, also called harvest flies (and, incorrectly, locusts), possess one of the most complex of the insect sound-producing organs. There are many species of cicadas and all have similar life histories except for the length of the immature life underground. The newly hatched cicada falls to the ground from the plant stem or leaf stem where the eggs were laid, and burrows into the earth until it finds a suitable juicy root. There it stays, sucking sap until it is ready to dig its way out of the ground with its enlarged front feet, shed its skin, and spend its brief adult life in the trees. Most of the cicadas that people hear in the late summer are probably the ones that spend two years underground. The periodical cicada—or as it is frequently called, seventeen-year locust, *Magicicada septendecim*—lives in the ground for 17 years. There is a closely related cicada, found in the southern United States, that lives in the ground for only 13 years (*See Cicada*).

As a rule the female cicada is silent, but in a very few species the female is as apt as the male. The "song" of a male cicada is produced by a pair of "drums" in the abdomen. These drums, or chambers, are covered by two plates called *opercula*. The drums vibrate by the action of a pair of powerful muscles, and the sound can be modified variously by the cicada through so-called sounding boards.

In ancient Greece cicadas were regarded as almost divine. The Greeks kept them in cages to hear them sing, wrote lyric poetry about them, and wore images of cicadas as hair ornaments. Their high regard for these insects is shown by the fact that the emblem of the science of music was a cicada upon a harp and the song of the cidada was the name given to the sound of the harp.

The Carolina locust, a short-horned grasshopper, makes crackling sounds while in flight by rubbing the margins of its hind wings against the surface of its fore wings

D. Sounds produced by friction of one part of the body against another part. Many Orthoptera (grasshoppers and their relatives) make sounds by this method. They are the insect "fiddlers" and most of the insect music that people hear in the summer time is made by them. The monotonous, simple tones of the cricket make the first insect chorus of spring and the last chorus in the fall. By mid-summer the grasshoppers and katydids and crickets, playing their various notes in strange rhythms, make up the orchestra that plays without interruption from dawn to dark and dark to dawn again. Only the males are equipped with the sound-making apparatus.

The short-horned grasshoppers or lo-custs have antennae much shorter than the body. Some species make a rasping sound by rubbing their hind legs against their front wings, or wing covers. When the grasshopper is at rest, the rear wings are folded like a fan underneath the front wings. There are rows of tiny spines on the hind legs and when these are scraped against the tough wings, the resulting sound is much like that produced by scraping the teeth of a small comb across the thumbnail.

Some short-horned grasshoppers have a very simple method of making sound. While in flight, they rub the upper surface of the costal (upper) margin of the hind wings upon the lower surface of the thickened veins of the forewings. The crackling flight of the very common Carolina locust is produced in this manner.

Other short-horned grasshoppers, the ones having gaily colored hind wings, rattle these wings while in flight. They are sometimes called the "castanet" grasshoppers. Formerly it was thought that the sound was made by the hind wings hitting against the front ones, but apparently the process is like that of vigorously opening and closing a fan.

Some species of short-horned grass-hoppers have no sound-making equipment on legs or wings but they sometimes make all the motions of fiddling without producing sound.

Most insects do not have definite ears, but grasshoppers and their relatives do have structures that are hearing or-gans. These structures of short-horned grasshoppers are located on the sides of the first segment of the abdomen. They are small, almost circular discs and can be seen when the wings are lifted out of the way. The "ears" of the long-horned or meadow grasshoppers and of the katydids and the crickets are on the upper part of the tibiae of their front legs.

The long-horned grasshoppers, the katydids, and the crickets all have long, threadlike antennae, and the apparatus for making sound is quite different from that of their short-horned relatives. The males of the "long-horns" fiddle by rubbing the under side of one forewing over the upper side of the other. The heavy rib that runs across the under side of each front wing has a series of ridges or teeth, like a file. The upper side of the wing has a rough area; when the wings are moved against each other from side to side, the little file rubs against the rough place and sets the wings into very rapid vibration, and a high, but in many species, soft and pleasing note is produced. When these insects fiddle, their leaflike front wings act as sounding boards, just as when a violin string is set to vibrating by the rosined bow, the tone produced is amplified by the instrument's sounding board.

The meadow grasshoppers, members of the longhorned tribe, live in fields and meadows, and "fiddle" all day long. The music is a very rapid, pleasant whirring, associated with hot summer afternoons and the smell of hayfields. However, some common meadow grasshoppers sing in the evening.

Katydids are beautiful green insects that live high in trees and shrubs where they are practically invisible. The wing covers are finely veined and very leaflike in both form and color. Although katydids are seldom seen, the rasping notes of the male may be heard on dark, cloudy days as well as in the evening and at night. High in the tree, the katydid clings to a branch, usually with its head down, scraping the file on the left wing across the rough surface of the right wing to produce the rasping argument: *Katy did, Katy did, did, did.* Other species may seem to say: *She didn't, she didn't, she didn't.*

Crickets are certainly the most popular of the insect musicians. Many different species contribute to the summer symphony, including the small, brown, ground crickets chirping in the grass and flower beds, the tree crickets trilling for hours night after night, and the common black field cricket fiddling in the sunshine.

One of the small tree dwellers, the snowy tree cricket, *Oecanthus niveus,* is also called the "temperature" cricket because it chirps more times per minute when the weather is warm than when it is cold. The temperature can be estimated roughly if one counts the number of chirps in 15 seconds and adds 40. The result is the temperature on the Fahrenheit scale. As a matter of fact, many, if not all, of the activities of insects are more rapid at higher than at lower temperatures.

The light brown European house cricket, *Gryllus domesticus,* is the "cricket on the hearth" praised in English poetry and story. It is sometimes found in homes and greenhouses in this country. The nightly chirping of one cricket on the hearth can be very pleasing, but in English dwellings they are frequently real pests.

Cricket Pets

The common black field crickets make interesting pets. A pair of these insects kept in a simple homemade cage is no more trouble than a goldfish, and many people find the crickets far more entertaining. Perhaps the simplest cage is a lantern globe or glass lamp chimney set in a flowerpot filled with earth or on a plaster of Paris base. If the globe is set over the soil in a flowerpot the soil should be kept damp. The crickets will eat almost anything—bread, pieces of apple or other fresh fruits, lettuce, and occasionally a bit of raw meat. They should be fed only a little at a time. A piece of crumpled paper towel or newspaper kept slightly damp will provide water and a necessary hiding place. The captive crickets can be observed firsthand and a person can see for himself how they "make their music."

The adult male cricket does the chirping. He can be distinguished from the female by this activity and by the fact that the female has a very conspicuous ovipositor at the end of her abdomen. When the cricket begins to chirp he raises his wings above the body and they can be seen moving rapidly from side to side, the right wing over the left wing. With the aid of a hand lens an observer can see the teeth on the under side of the heavy rib, running across the front part of each forewing This rasping organ is called a file. A hardened area near the end of the file is the scraper. The sound is produced when the wings are held in such a position that the scraper of one wing will rasp on the file of the other. This motion throws the wings into vibration and produces the sound. Observation also reveals the space that is clear of veins in about the center of each wing. This is the crickets' "sounding board." Females do not have these structures on their wings. The adult life of a male cricket lasts about a month and he spends a large part of his life chirping.

All the grasshoppers and their relatives, as well as the cicada, can be kept in cages and their habits observed. For the larger species a terrarium with fresh sod at the bottom provides a satisfactory cage. —A.K.B.

Recommended Reading

A Book About Bees — Edwin Way Teale. Indiana University Press. Bloomington, Indiana.
Entomology for Introductory Courses — Robert Matheson. Comstock Publishing Company, Inc. Ithaca, New York.
Field Book of Insects — Frank E. Lutz. G. P. Putnam's Sons, New York.
Golden Nature Guide; Insects — H. S. Zim and Clarence Cottam. Simon &·Schuster, Inc., New York.
Handbook of Nature Study — Anna B. Comstock. Comstock Publishing Company, Inc. Ithaca, New York.
The Insect Guide — Ralph B. Swain. Doubleday & Company, Garden City, New York.
Insects in Their World — SuZan N. Swain. Garden City Books, Garden City, New York.
An Introduction to the Study of Insects — Donald J. Borror and Dwight M. DeLong. Rinehart & Company, New York.
The Junior Book of Insects — Edwin Way Teale. E. P. Dutton & Co., Inc., New York.
Living Insects of the World — Alexander B. and Elsie B. Klots. Doubleday & Comapny, Garden City, New York.
A Lot of Insects — Frank E. Lutz. G. P. Putnam s Sons, New York.

Insect Values

There is a feeling on the part of many people that if Noah, in the long, long ago, had held up a *No Trespassing* sign and denied insects entrance to the Ark, the world would have been spared a great deal of trouble. But they are mistaken. Noah knew what he was about. Insect lives are so closely enmeshed with man's that he cannot do without them.

Pollinators

As pollinators alone many insects are deserving of protection. Suppose they had perished in the Flood? What then? The chances are that today people would be largely dependent upon bananas for breakfast, if they wanted to enjoy a staple fruit. Because the pollen of oranges, plums, figs, apples, blackberries, raspberries, grapes, and sweet cherries is moist, it is not easily carried by the wind. But the pollen does adhere to the bodies of visiting bees, wasps, flies, moths, and butterflies that, in their ceaseless quest for nectar, are inadvertently used as pollen distributors. Except in the case of bananas, which have dry pollen, insect services are important in the formation of the more common fruits.

In commercial orchards honeybees are employed as pollinating agents because their activities are subject to man s control. Their bodies are hairy and their hind legs modified to carry the precious dust. They are inclined to work one type of blossom to the exclusion of all others so long as the nectar flow is abundant. One colony of honeybees to an acre of orchard, under favorable flight conditions, has been known to increase the apple yield by 350 percent.

With fruit scarce in an insect-free world, except for bananas, what choice of vegetables would there be for luncheon? There would be corn, because corn is a grass and grasses are wind-pollinated. On the other hand, tomatoes, peas, beans, cauliflower, squash, onions, cabbages, and most other food vegetables will not set seed or bear fruit to any great extent without the aid of insects. They could be pollinated by hand, or perhaps stimulated to produce by other artificial means, but the cost to the consumer would be staggering.

By dinner time, in an insect-free world, a meat course would be welcomed. Pork would be plentiful because pigs eat corn, and so would beef and mutton because cattle and sheep are grazing animals; but the latter meats would be of inferior grade because the best forage crops would be lacking. Legumes, such as clover and alfalfa, require insects for the mass production of seed. Poultry and marine fish would be on the menu; but one would search in vain for those freshwater game fish that are dependent upon aquatic insects or insect-eating organisms for food.

There would be no flowering plants to adorn the banquet table. In fact, it is doubtful if there were any before the advent of insects. Coffee, tea, cocoa, and the best soft drinks would be lacking, as would chocolates, salted nuts, and after-dinner smokes. Silk dresses would not grace a lady's wardrobe, and neither cotton nor linen tablecloths would be possible. The charm of subtle music and gay plumage would largely have gone from the garden because most songbirds would have disappeared along with their favorite food.

There is no denying the fact that some insects are exceedingly destructive. They are responsible for the loss of about 20 percent of the fruit crop each year. But it must be remembered that if it were not for certain other insects, there would be almost no fruit crop at all.

By pollinating legumes, such as clover and vetch, insects provide desirable cover crops to anchor top soil against erosion. Without this valuable soil the yield of orchards, gardens, forests, and plains could not be maintained except at prohibitive cost. Because legumes also have nitrogen-fixing bacteria in their roots, they enrich the soil and thereby cut down on the need for certain commercial fertilizers.

Soil Conditioners

The value to the soil of ground-burrowing insects is impossible to compute. An estimated 95 percent of all insects spend at least a part of their lives underground. Charles Darwin is the authority for the statement that 50,000 earthworms can turn up 18 tons of soil per year; but insects are often more numerous than earthworms and far more active. Ants, grubs, beetles, and crickets are forever cultivating the earth, bringing up subsoil and burying organic matter; and in death their own bodies enrich the earth.

The character of the humus in the soil is changed for the better by exposure to the insects' grinding jaws; and the tunnels they make help to absorb rain water, prevent run-off, and carry oxygen to needy plant roots. Their beneficial effect upon the arable surface of the globe may, in some places at least, be even more important than that of earthworms.

Scavengers

About 17 percent of all insect species are scavengers. One of their accomplishments is that they keep nature's premises neat and clean. In India alone scarab beetles are said to bury 60,000 tons of decaying matter daily.

Burying beetles, scarcely an inch long, with black and red markings, are clever at disposing of the dead. They will even bury rabbits and squirrels, giants compared with themselves, by digging the earth from beneath them. Often they work cooperatively. Four such beetles in 50 days were observed to bury three small birds, four frogs, two fish, one mole, two grasshoppers, the entrails of one small fish, and two pieces of ox liver. Like dogs, they will often lay by far more than they can readily consume. Carrion beetles, certain ants, and blow-fly maggots are also noted land scavengers, whereas seaside earwigs work along the tidal zone, and there are large scavenger beetles that live in fresh water.

Although insects are important scavengers in their own right, they are perhaps even more valuable in the general economy of nature as aids to bacterial and fungus decay. By tunneling through the bark of dead trees and the skin of dead animals, they make dark and damp pockets that hasten the disintegration of these lesser organisms. Without this service the earth in time would become strewn with a vast accumulation of dead, unchanging bodies within which would be locked the elements essential to green plant growth and even to man's existence. Anyone who has visited a region after a forest fire or a hurricane, and then visited it again several years later, can appreciate the importance of quick reconversion in which insects play so prominent a part.

One is not accustomed to think of borers and termites as beneficial. They are not when they destroy live trees, lumber, or buildings; but when they attack dead trees, they are simply hastening the breakdown of the old for reuse in nature's building-up process.

Predators

Approximately 16 percent of all insect species are predacious, but that does not mean that their actions are entirely commendable. Many of them are indiscriminate in their habits, attacking useful insects and spiders as well as pests.

The Chinese praying mantis, with its three inches of body and grasping front legs, can strike awe in many a stout heart. When a large object approaches, it rears up in defiance, spreads its wings fanlike, straddles its four hind legs and erect its two front legs in an attitude of prayer. Alert for any eventuality, it cocks its tiny head with bulging eyes, then strikes without warning. The victims comprise any insects it can overpower. One praying mantis at a single meal consumed a spider, a daddy longlegs, and three grasshoppers. Egg masses of the Chinese praying mantis arrived in this country on nursery stock about fifty years ago. Since then it has increased to become commonplace in many gardens.

Some insect predators not equipped with grasping front legs use speed or ingenuity to capture live food. Dragonflies belong in this category. They will fashion their legs into a scoop net and dart about in the air, gathering up gnats, flies, and mosquitoes. Upon alighting they can eat their catch at their leisure. Like other swift fliers, their appetites are enormous. In two hours one individual consumed 40 houseflies. The adults are commonly known as mosquito hawks, a name that might also be applied to their aquatic nymphs which feed upon mosquito wrigglers.

Another predator is the doodlebug, which sets a trap for its dinner. It is a soft-bodied creature, scarcely a quarter inch long, with nippers like ice tongs for jaws. They can be found at the bottom of cone-shaped pits, which they frequently dig in soft earth at the base of trees where ants are active. If an ant approaches and carelessly tumbles into a pit, its fate is generally sealed. Should it try to escape, the doodlebug will either pelt it with small stones, which it tosses with its head, or wiggle a front leg to cause a landslide. Once the ant is within reach, the doodlebug's large jaws will seize it and suck out its life's blood.

Parasites

About 12 percent of all insect species are parasites, many of them important in the control of destructive caterpillars, grubs, and other pests. The United States Department of Agriculture raises a wide assortment of insect parasites to use against the Oriental fruit moth, the European corn borer, and similar undesirable foreign guests. In the country of their origin they might have been good citizens, but removed from their natural controls they prove otherwise.

The Japanese beetle, a comparatively recent stowaway in nursery stock from the Orient, is a menace to lawns, grape arbors, rose gardens, and many crops. Its numbers have been greatly reduced in some areas by the introduction of a black wasp known as *Tiphia,* which lays its eggs on Japanese beetle grubs feeding beneath the ground on grass roots.

Another parasite is the ichneumon fly, which happens to be a native of this country. One may see it in the spring, drilling holes through the bark of unhealthy sugar maple trees. Its yellowish-brown body is scarcely 1½ inches long, but appended to it is a tail-like ovipositor maybe twice that length. As it drills, it loops its "tail" around like a jug handle. Then it sinks the ovipositor down, sometimes almost to the hilt, until it strikes the tunnel made by a *Tremex* borer. At last it has found its mark. The ovipositor then performs its normal function of laying eggs, and the eggs hatch into small white larvae, which follow along the tunnel until they find the borer. The borer is attacked and consumed, and the tree it might have killed is saved from further injury.

Weed Destroyers

Although insects have not been widely used for the control of weeds, it has been shown in certain cases that their services for this purpose can be invaluable. Specialized feeders are employed for the most part and against introduced weeds. The prickly pear cactus is an outstanding example of a plant out of place that has been successfully combatted with insects.

Manufacturers

Products of insect industry have been

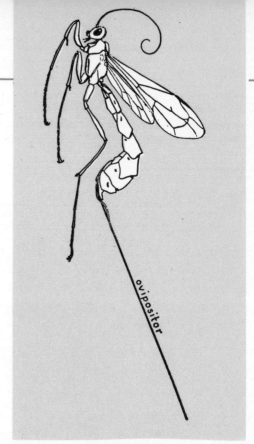

Ichneumon fly

utilized by man since the beginning of time. They furnish the basis for many articles of everyday commerce that have become an essential part of our present civilization. The Greeks and Romans made dyes from the bodies of scale insects found on red oak, and the Aztecs used the bodies of cochineal insects found on cactus plants. Modern man thought himself independent of this source of supply when aniline dyes were discovered; but in World War I the Allies cut off from Germany and not knowing the secret of obtaining satisfactory crimson dyes from coal tar, were glad enough to return once again to insects.

Lac insects have been a source of wealth in India for over 2,500 years. Although adult specimens are no larger than a dot and red in color, they can in proportion to their size excrete an amazing amount of resinous fluid, which hardens to give them protection. Man removes this resin, refines it, and sells it as shellac. Shellac goes into the manufacture of beads, varnish, hats, bracelets, shoe polish, billiard balls, phonograph records, and many other products.

The silkworm has been providing sheer thread to the delight of human vanity for 4,000 years. It is said to take the threads from 5,000 cocoons to make one kimono. Silkworm gut for tying trout flies is made from the tubular glands of the silkworm itself.

The only sweetening 2,000 years ago was provided by bees. In spite of recent competition from cane and beet sugar, honey is still an important item in cooking, cough drops, candy, and cosmetics. More than 200 million pounds of honey are produced annually in apiaries, and more than 4 million pounds of beeswax. The wax has been used for waterproofing uniforms, ammunition, and for electric wiring. Today it is employed in numberless surprising ways: sealing wax, dental wax, grafting wax, church candles, shoe polish, furniture polish, carbon paper, lithographic ink, etching, textiles, cosmetics, and deodorants.

Food

In many countries insects are relished for food. Mexicans make a special cake of water-boatman eggs; East Indians use ground locusts in their curry powder; South Africans roast termites like peanuts and eat them by the handfuls; and the people of southern France like the sour taste of certain ants. Mealworms are raised by the billions for bird food.

These examples of the usefulness of insects can be multiplied many times to show that creatures that might at first seem only pests do serve man in countless ways.   — B.E.

Recommended Reading

The Biological Control of Insects — Harvey L. Sweetman. Comstock Publishing Company Philadelphia.
Curious History of Insects — Frank Cowan. J.B. Lippincott & Company, Philadelphia.
Destructive and Useful Insects — Metcalf and Flint. McGraw-Hill Book Company, Inc., New York and London.
Insects in Their World — SuZan N. Swain. Garden City Books, Garden City, New York.
The Insect World — Louis Figuier. D. Appleton & Company, New York.
An Introduction to the Study of Insects — Donald J. Borror and Dwight M. DeLong. Holt, Rinehart, and Winston, Inc., New York.
The Junior Book of Insects — Edwin Way Teale. E.P. Dutton & Company, New York.
Living Insects of the World — Alexander B. and Elsie B. Klots. Doubleday & Company, Garden City, New York.
The World of Insects — Paul Pesson. McGraw-Hill, New York.
1001 Questions Answered About Insects — Alexander B. and Elsie B. Klots. Dodd, Mead & Company, New York.

Insects in Winter

Insects, like other living things, are adapted in various ways to endure the cold of winter. In the autumn millions of insects die, but many others live through the winter as eggs, larvae, pupae, or adults. Most insects pass through metamorphosis, or distinct changes in form, during growth. This metamorphosis may be complete, as with the butterfly, which hatches from the egg as a caterpillar (larva), passes through the dormant chrysalis stage (pupa), and emerges as an adult winged butterfly. Moths, bees, wasps, ants, beetles, and true flies have complete metamorphosis. Other insects, such as grasshoppers, crickets, and roaches, hatch from the egg in forms not unlike the adult and develop gradually. They are said to have incomplete metamorphosis.

With the first warm days of spring insects will become active. Where and how have they spent the winter?

Some insects pass the winter as adults. The queen bumblebee, a fertilized female, spends the winter in a snug retreat and in spring makes her nest, often in a deserted burrow of a field mouse. The honeybee, the wasp that makes paper nests in the summer, and ants also hibernate as adults. Some adult moths and butterflies also hide away during the winter. The mourning cloak is the largest butterfly that hibernates in the adult stage. It finds a hiding place under the loose bark of a tree or under a rock.

Many two-winged flies, such as houseflies, gnats, and mosquitoes, pass the winter as adults. Hibernating mosquitoes may be found during the winter in barns, cellars and other protected places. When cold weather comes, many adult water insects swim to the bottom and bury themselves in the mud, where they remain during the winter. Such insects include water boatmen, backswimmers, giant water bugs, and water striders.

Many beetles overwinter as adults. Tiger beetles, ground beetles, the lady beetle, and the Colorado potato beetle hide away in burrows in the ground or in other suitable shelters. The black-and-white adult click beetle, however, flies throughout the season.

Many insects overwinter in the pupal stage. The pupae of some moths are protected by cocoons; those not so protected are known as naked pupae. Butterfly pupae are called chrysalises and are not protected by cocoons. The giant silkworm moths— *Cecropia, Promethia, Polyphemus, Cynthia,* and *Luna*—pass the winter in tough silk cocoons fastened securely to the branches of trees. In the spring the moths emerge, mate, lay their eggs, and die. These winged adults have no mouthparts and do not eat. Many moths, including the common tomato worm moth, spin no cocoon or other covering and hibernate as pupae in the ground.

Many butterflies hibernate as chrysalises. They include the beautiful swallowtail butterflies and the common cabbage butterfly.

During the winter the pupae of many other insects may be found in the soil, in dead trees, under logs and rubbish, and in other protected places.

Some insects pass the winter as larvae. Insects such as dragonflies, damselflies, and crickets have no true larval

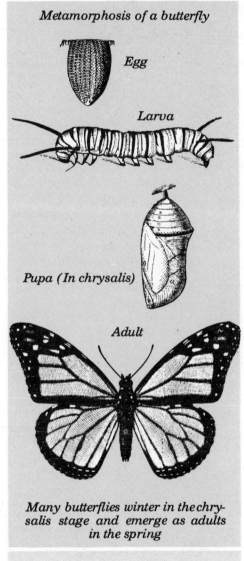

Metamorphosis of a butterfly

Egg

Larva

Pupa (In chrysalis)

Adult

Many butterflies winter in the chrysalis stage and emerge as adults in the spring

Back swimmer

Colorado potato beetle

Many insects winter over as adults. Some bury themselves in the soil or in the mud of pond bottoms

May-beetle pupa

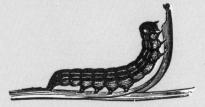

Army worm (Late summer broods)

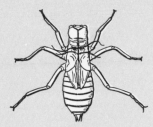

Dragonfly nymph

Many insects spend the winter in the larval stage

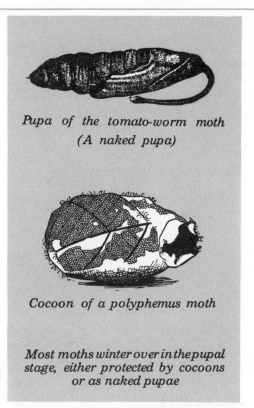

Pupa of the tomato-worm moth (A naked pupa)

Cocoon of a polyphemus moth

Most moths winter over in the pupal stage, either protected by cocoons or as naked pupae

stage, and the young resemble the adults. Many of these young, called nymphs, hibernate. They include the water nymphs of dragonflies, damselflies, and mayflies. The field cricket usually passes the winter in the egg stage, but some individuals hibernate as nymphs.

The caterpillars of a few moths and butterflies may be found in the winter under rocks and boards on the ground, in the soil, in bark, and under leaves. Some cutworms, the larvae of noctuid moths, hibernate in snug underground cells, and the larvae of the silver crescent butterfly crawl into one of these ready-made shelters. for the winter.

Many beetles hibernate as larvae, or grubs. The fat white grub of the may beetle burrows into the soil for the winter. Some species of two-winged flies pass the winter as larvae, or maggots. Larvae of the horsefly winter in the soil. Many insects overwinter in the egg stage. Most grasshoppers and their relatives, such as crickets, katydids, walkingsticks, and praying mantises lay their eggs in the fall and the young hatch out in the spring. Grasshoppers and crickets lay their eggs in the ground; the praying mantis deposits her eggs on twigs in a mass protected by a frothy brownish substance; the walkingstick clinging to a branch, drops her eggs singly to the ground; and the katydid places her eggs in the bark of trees.

Many of the true bugs, plant lice and

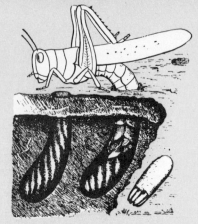

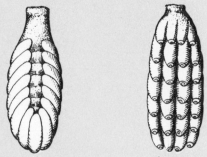

Grasshopper eggs are deposited in the soil in an egg pod (above). The eggs are usually laid in 4 rows and average 28 in number (below)

Grasshoppers are typical of insects that spend the winter in the egg stage

their relatives, live through the winter in the egg stage. Some plant lice lay their eggs in the bark of trees.

A few moths hibernate as eggs. The common tent caterpillar is a good example. In July the eggs are laid in a band encircling a small twig and covered with a waterproof varnish. The eggs of the bagworm are laid by the female moth in the cocoon from which she emerges. Eggs thus laid pass the winter in the cocoon and in the spring hatch into caterpillars.

INSECTICIDE

Any agent used in killing insects is an insecticide. The commonest insecticides are chemicals of various sorts.

Insecticidal chemicals include the following categories: inorganic chemicals, such as lead arsenate and copper sulfate; naturally occurring organic chemicals derived from plants, such as nicotine sulfate, pyrethrum, rotenone, and ryania; and synthetic organic chemicals.

The synthetic chemicals are of three large classes: (1) the chlorinated hydrocarbons (aldrin, aramite, benzene hexachloride (BHC), chlordate, DDT, endrin, heptachlor, methoxychlor, and toxaphene; (2) the organic phosphorus compounds (organophosphates) such as malathion, parathion, phosdrin, TEEP, and others; and (3) the carbamate compounds represented by sevin.

It is the synthetic chemical insecticides, widely used since World War II that have been the subject of great controversy in recent years. (*See also under DDT*)

Audubon Honor to Rachel Carson

[Editor's Note: During the annual dinner of the National Audubon Society at the Hotel Roosevelt on December 3, 1963, Rachel Carson, author of the book *Silent Spring,* which alerted the general public to an awareness of the dangers of chemical insecticides, was awarded the Audubon Medal. The award is made from time to time to persons whom the National Audubon Society feels have accomplished outstanding work in conservation (*See Audubon Medal*)].

Miss Carson, the first woman to receive the Audubon Medal for distinguished service to conservation, responded as follows:

"I come before you tonight to receive the Audubon Medal with mingled feelings of pride and humility. The roll call of names of those who have received this medal before me includes many whose place in the history of American conservation is both illustrious and secure.

"I have known at firsthand the character and achievements of most of these men; my years of government service were carried out under two of them. To be adjudged worthy to join this distinguished company is an honor I receive not lightly, but with deep appreciation and gratitude.

"I am mindful, too, that a prophet is not always honored in his own country—but the National Audubon Society is my country—I belong to it—and from its own strength and devotion to the cause of conservation I have drawn strength and inspiration, as have many thousands of others.

"For we all are united in a common cause. It is a proud cause, which we may serve secure in the knowledge that the earth will be better for our efforts. It is a cause that has no end: There is no point at which we shall say, 'Our work is finished.' We build on the achievements of those who have gone before us; let us, in turn, build strong foundations for those who will take up the work when we must lay it down.

"Recently I read Secretary (Stewart L.) Udall's book, *The Quiet Crisis*, which is a fine summary of the history of conservation in America. It is a history that on the one hand inspires dismay, on the other a measure of hope. It inspires dismay at the ruthless stripping of timber lands, the relentless slaughter of wildlife, the reckless raid on the resources of a rich and beautiful land—but a land not inexhaustible.

"It inspires hope and courage because even the darkest hours have brought forth men who, though their numbers were but a handful, nevertheless contrived to save for us enough that we may at least glimpse the grandeur of this continent as it was a few centuries ago.

"Over the decades and the centuries, the scenes and the actors change. Yet the central theme remains—the greed and the shortsightedness of the few who would deprive the many of their rightful heritage.

"It is a theme supported by the false assurances that whatever is financially profitable is good for the nation and for mankind. These assurances were offered in the days of the timber barons and the land grabbers; they are heard today.

"If the crisis that now confronts us is even more urgent than those of the early years of the century—and I believe it is—this is because of wholly new factors peculiar to our own time.

"These are, first of all, the phenomenal growth of the human population, threatening to over-run its own environment in a way that can bring only deep concern to thoughtful students of population problems.

"The second factor is a corollary of the first: that as people and their demands increase, there is a smaller share of the earth's resources for each of us to use and enjoy. There is less clean water, less uncontaminated air; there are fewer forests, fewer unspoiled wilderness areas.

"The third reason is the introduction of new and dangerous contaminants into soil, water, air, and the bodies of plants and animals as our new technology spreads its poisons and its discarded wastes over the land.

"And so we live in a time when change comes rapidly—a time when much of that change is, at least for long periods, irrevocable. This is what makes our own task so urgent. It is not often that a generation is challenged, as we today are challenged. For what we fail to do—what we let go by default—can perhaps never be done.

"I take courage, however, in the fact that the conservation effort has a broader base than ever before. There is more organized effort; there are many more individuals who are conscious of conservation problems and who are striving, in their own communities or on the national scene, to solve these problems.

"The educational programs carried on by the National Audubon Society have played a distinguished role in bringing this about.

"And so the effort must and shall go on. Though the task will never be ended we must engage in it with a patience that refuses to be turned aside, with determination to overcome obstacles, and with pride that it is our privilege to contribute so greatly."   —R.C.

How Insects Resist Insecticides

Heavy doses and high lethal rates kill all but the toughest insects which, in turn, breed resistant offspring.

Laboratory experiment shows how flies develop resistance. Similar resistance occurs among insects in the wild, although possibly to a less spectacular degree. Higher doses and more lethal poisons are no solution. In Nebraska, resistance of the corn rootworm to aldrin caused sprayers to increase the dose by 100 times.

1. DDT KILLS 98 PERCENT

Resistant survivors

2. SAME DOSE NOW KILLS 85 PERCENT (*Survivors bred resistant generation*)

More survivors

3. DOSE NOW KILLS ONLY 50 PERCENT (*Resistant generations multiply*)

Half are now resistant